'You'll get over ... **touching her h** ...

'Will I?'

'I really am sorry you had to be hurt,' he said, with a gentleness Erin hadn't expected.

'That's why you waited for me here. You knew I'd come stumbling down the road, bawling my eyes out like some wretched soap-opera character. And there you'd be, Brett Mallory, strong, macho, ready to mop up the tears.'

Dear Reader

Spring is just around the corner; for some this new season may bring a dose of 'spring-fever'—perhaps starting a new diet, thinking about a holiday, or cleaning your house from top to bottom. Others will welcome the longer, lighter days and the first flowers. Whatever your mood, this month Mills & Boon has a great selection of bright, fresh romances, with tempting backgrounds: Greece, Africa, Taiwan and the spectacular Winter Carnival in Venice to name but a few...and we're planning plenty more in the year to come!

The Editor

Rosemary Carter was born in South Africa, but has lived in Canada for many years with her husband and her three children. Although her home is on the prairies, not far from the beautiful Rockies, she still retains her love of the South African bushveld, which is why she likes to set her stories there. Both Rosemary and her husband enjoy concerts, theatre, opera and hiking in the mountains. Reading was always her passion, and led to her first attempts at writing stories herself.

NIGHT OF
THE SCORPION

BY

ROSEMARY CARTER

MILLS & BOON LIMITED
ETON HOUSE   18-24 PARADISE ROAD
RICHMOND   SURREY   TW9 1SR

First published in Great Britain 1993
by Mills & Boon Limited

© Rosemary Carter 1993

Australian copyright 1993
Philippine copyright 1993
This edition 1993

ISBN 0 263 77933 5

Set in Times Roman 10 on 12 pt.
01-9303-50491 C

Made and printed in Great Britain

CHAPTER ONE

PRESSING her face against the window, Erin tried to look through the blackness beyond the railway tracks. With the approach of dawn, the sky had lightened just a little, so that it was now possible to discern fences and light standards and even the gaunt shapes of trees.

Darkness had descended quite soon after the train had left Johannesburg the previous evening. Erin's only travelling companion, a tiny, sparrow-faced elderly woman, had closed her eyes almost immediately, but Erin, a stranger in a new country, on the verge of a new life, had been far too excited to sleep.

The elderly woman was now beginning to stir. She stretched, sat up, splashed herself with fragrant toilet water, then looked at Erin.

'Morning, dear. Have you just woken as well?'

'I've been awake all night.'

'Heavens, you must be exhausted.'

'I'm too keyed up for that,' said Erin. 'I've been looking forward to this day for so long.'

'I thought last night that I heard an American accent,' said the woman. 'In South Africa on holiday, are you?'

'Actually, I'm Canadian, and I've come all this way to be married,' Erin told her.

'How exciting!'

'Yes, it is. Would you know how far we are from Nelspruit?'

The woman glanced at her watch. 'Not more than twenty minutes.'

'Great!'

Erin opened her bag and took out her cosmetic purse. When she had put on some lipstick and run a comb through her tumbled curls, she stood up to gather her belongings.

She was leaning out of the window when they drew into the Eastern Transvaal station. As the train lumbered slowly to a halt, she searched the faces of the people on the platform. To her disappointment, she did not see Jim.

'Never easy to spot a face in a crowd,' consoled the woman.

'My fiancé will be here to meet me,' Erin said confidently.

'I'm sure he will. Congratulations on your wedding, dear, and good luck with your new life.'

'Thank you so much,' Erin replied, as she made for the door of the compartment.

Her luggage was heavy, for she had packed into her suitcases as much as she could. What was left in Canada was stored in big cartons, labelled and addressed to a timber plantation a few hours' drive from Nelspruit. Erin's mother had instructions to send them by boat as soon as her daughter was settled.

She was struggling to heave the cases out of the train when a man's voice said, 'Need some help?'

Erin lifted a grateful face, but her smile faded as she took in the man who had spoken to her.

'No, thank you,' she said politely.

She recalled seeing him in Johannesburg. About to board the train, she had had a sudden sense of being watched, and, turning, she had found herself looking into a pair of dark, intelligent eyes set in a deeply tanned face with strong lines and high cheekbones. For a long moment their eyes had held, and then, as she'd remembered where she was going and why, Erin had deliberately turned a flushed face away.

The meeting of eyes had been unnerving, and she felt no less disconcerted again now. But she was determined not to show it.

Her gaze swept the platform once more, but Jim was nowhere in sight, and the train showed signs of proceeding further.

'Those cases look heavy,' said the stranger.

'They are,' Erin said, quite calmly. 'On second thoughts, I'd appreciate it very much if you could lift them off the train for me.'

The man leaned past her and swung the suitcases on to the platform, as easily as if they weighed no more than two bags of flour.

'What shall I do with them?' he asked, when Erin had thanked him.

'They'll be fine just here.'

'You'll be able to manage them on your own?' The expression in the dark eyes was sardonic.

'I won't have to. I'm being met.'

Once more his eyes held hers. Then his gaze moved over her face, and downwards, taking in her slim, shapely figure in a look that was so thoroughly male and assessing that it brought another angry flush to Erin's cheeks. He was tough, she thought. Confident. A man who was used to giving orders, and having them obeyed. Attractive too. And so sexy that he obviously took it for granted that no woman would ever refuse him anything he might want.

'If you're sure,' he said.

'Perfectly.'

He gave an unexpected grin, then turned. Watching him walk away, Erin wondered who he was, what he did, where he lived. Jim might know. And then she told herself that she would be a married woman soon, and, because of that, the man could have no place in her new life. She would not ask Jim about him.

Where was Jim anyway?

The station was beginning to empty. Some of the passengers had been met, others had already gone on their way alone. It was easy now to scan the faces of the people who were left, but Jim was not one of them.

For one awful moment Erin wondered if she would recognise her fiancé when she saw him. Theirs had been such a whirlwind courtship, and more than a year had passed since she had seen him last. Briefly, she closed her eyes and tried to bring a picture of Jim into her mind. She could not see his face, not exactly, and that concerned her a little. But he was of medium height, his hair was sandy, and his face was appealingly freckled. Yes, of course she would recognise him—foolish to think otherwise.

The minutes passed, and still Jim did not arrive, but Erin refused to let herself worry. He must have been delayed. The hour was so early, and as the manager of a timber plantation Jim had many responsibilities. That was it, of course. A problem had cropped up, and he had had to deal with it before driving to Nelspruit. Any moment now, the man she was engaged to would appear on the platform. They would embrace joyously, then they would drive together to the plantation. In a few days they would be married.

And still Jim did not come.

Erin glanced at her watch. Twenty minutes had gone by since the train had left. What was it Jim had said in his last letter? 'If by some chance I'm late—and I hope I won't be—wait for me at the Twin Palms Hotel. I'll meet you in the lobby.'

Erin had always been resourceful. Granddaughter of farming folk who had homesteaded on the prairies, she knew how to take care of herself. Leaving her luggage for a few minutes—nothing would happen to it—she found a taxi, asked the driver to help with her suitcases, then told him to drive her to the Twin Palms Hotel.

As the taxi left the station, Erin sat forward in her seat and stared out of the window in dismay. The sky was much lighter now, so that she was able to see her surroundings. Branches littered the ground. Trees were bent. Pools of water eddied on the ground. Debris was everywhere.

She turned to the driver. 'There must have been quite a storm here.'

'A whopper, lady,' he said cheerfully. 'One of the worst in years.'

'I had no idea!'

'Well, at least it's over now. They say the sun's out to stay. And here we are, lady, Twin Palms Hotel.'

The hotel was a low whitewashed building with two identical palm trees on either side of the main door. In front of the building was a garden with shrubs and a creeper that covered the walls, and here too Erin saw the destruction she had seen elsewhere: the fronds of the twin palms were torn and ragged, and the flowers of the creeper were scattered on the damp grass.

The taxi driver carried her luggage to the door of the hotel, where she paid and tipped him. Quickly she walked into the lobby.

Jim was not there.

Trying to suppress a feeling of growing disappointment, Erin went to the reception desk.

'My name is Erin Leroy, and I'm supposed to be meeting someone here. A Mr Saunders—Jim Saunders?'

'As far as I know, nobody by that name has been here today,' said the receptionist, in the accent that was beginning to sound familiar.

'Perhaps he called and left a message for me?'

'I'm afraid not.'

'He'll be arriving soon. Is there somewhere I can leave my luggage while I wait?' asked Erin.

The receptionist's manner was crisp and efficient. 'I'll get the porter to put your cases in a locked room, Miss Leroy. Perhaps you'd like to go and wait in the lounge in the meantime? It's through there . . .' She gestured.

'Will Jim find me there?'

'If he comes, I'll be sure to tell him where you are.'

When, not *if*, Erin thought, but did not say so.

So early in the morning, the lounge was already crowded with people, many of them commercial travellers, having a quick coffee and something to eat before hitting the road. Stopping in the doorway, Erin let her eyes go over the people in the hope of seeing a sandy-topped head and freckled face. But Jim was not here either.

After a moment, she found herself a vacant table, sat down, and ordered coffee and toasted cheese.

Where was Jim?

The food had just been brought to her table when she saw a face she knew. The man from the train had entered the lounge with two other men, and they were making their way to a table not far from Erin's. He had not seen her, not yet, but he would, for the chair he took faced hers.

Erin tried to concentrate her attention firmly on the door through which, at any moment now, her fiancé would walk. But it was difficult not to let her gaze wander. Without meaning to, she looked at the nearby table—and found the man watching her. His eyebrows lifted in a question, and Erin allowed herself a slight smile before looking in the direction of the door once more.

The waiter appeared, and she asked for more coffee. She tried to shrug away a flicker of apprehension. There had to be a good reason for Jim's absence, and when they met he would tell her what it was. It was only fatigue after the long journey that was beginning to make her feel so uneasy.

Half an hour passed. At the nearby table, the man from the train still sat with his companions. Without looking his way, Erin felt his eyes on her face, more often than she liked. She was tempted to get up, to sit elsewhere, but she knew that to do so would reveal insecurity.

There was one thing she could do, however, and should have done earlier. In her diary was the phone number of the timber plantation. Standing up, and without looking at the man, she left her table and walked purposefully out of the lounge.

In the lobby was a public phone. Erin put a coin in the slot, dialled the number written in her diary, and waited. A few moments of silence, then a loud, shrill sound. Again she tried. Again that same shrill sound.

Now what? she wondered, as she returned to her table in the lounge. For the first time, she realised quite how far from home she was, and how alone. Save for Jim, she knew nobody in the entire country. There was not a soul she could turn to for help. Not a person she could even talk to. Except for one... Briefly she met the curious, watching eyes of the man from the train.

The men at the nearby table paid their bill, and stood up to go. Out of the corner of her eye Erin saw that the man from the train was standing too. She felt, suddenly, as if she was being abandoned—and chided herself for being irrational. It was all just a part of feeling so alone...

And then there he was at her table, seeming to tower over her. She had the sense of an uncompromising maleness.

'Still being met?'

'Yes,' Erin said brightly.

Dark brows lifted. 'Sure about that?'

'My fiancé knows I'm here. He won't let me down.'

'*Fiancé?*'

Erin saw a strange look in the man's eyes, but it was quickly gone.

'I have a feeling I surprised you,' she said, a little uncertainly.

'I should have known, I suppose.' His eyes were hooded now. 'We don't get many Canadians in this part of the country.'

'Actually, most people I've met since leaving home have taken me for American,' she said.

'They would.'

Erin felt even more uneasy now, though she could not have said why. 'I think you know who I am,' she began.

'Your name is Erin Leroy.' It was a statement rather than a question.

'Yes, that's right! If you know that, then you must know Jim.'

'I know him.'

'Wait . . .' she said, as he made to move away from her table.

He looked at her. His body, six feet two at least, seemed filled with urgency and purpose. He had to be in his early thirties, Erin thought, although the fluidity of his movements could have belonged to a much younger man.

'You know my name, but I don't know yours,' she said.

'Brett. Brett Mallory.'

And then he walked away.

The lounge seemed curiously empty when Brett Mallory was gone. Despite the fact that almost every table was occupied, an energy seemed to have vanished from the room.

Erin looked around for the waiter. When she saw him, she beckoned him to her table and asked for her bill. He was back minutes later. Erin opened her wallet. She was not yet familiar with the South African currency, so it took her a few seconds to count out the amount she needed and to work out a reasonable tip.

She had always had the ability to make a decision and to act on it. She knew she could not dither now, for if she did it could well be too late. Quickly she left the lounge, crossed the lobby, and walked out of the hotel. On her way in, she had noticed only the flamboyance of the battered garden; now she saw that a paved drive led from the street, past the entrance to the lobby, and around the building.

In the car park behind the hotel she saw Brett Mallory immediately. He was loading boxes into a long silver car. He had removed the jacket he had been wearing, and his short-sleeved shirt, bare to the elbows, revealed arms that were tanned and muscular. He was a superb figure of a man. Erin stared at him, feeling a little breathless for a moment. Then she remembered that she was to be married in a few days' time, and that she had absolutely no business thinking about the physical attributes of a man other than her fiancé. Lips tight suddenly, she walked up to him.

'Mr Mallory...' she began.

He turned. 'Well, Miss Leroy?'

'May I have a ride with you?'

'Jim will be here tomorrow.' His voice was dry.

'I don't want to wait,' she explained.

'Why not? You could take a room here. As a hotelier, I can tell you it's comfortable enough, I've stayed here myself.'

'I'd rather not,' Erin told him.

'Nelspruit is a pretty town, Miss Leroy. Do a bit of sightseeing. Have a meal. See a movie, if you want to. And tomorrow you'll go to the station and meet Jim.'

'I want to get to the plantation today,' she insisted.

'Can't wait to see your man?' The gaze that swept her face was enigmatic.

'Yes, I want to see him.'

'Do yourself a favour, and wait until tomorrow.'

Brett Mallory's opposition was beginning to make Erin angry. 'Is the thought of giving me a ride so disagreeable?' she asked.

For the second time since she'd met him, she was treated to a look that seemed to take in every inch of her face and body. Forcing herself to still a sudden trembling, she shifted her eyes.

'Disagreeable?' Brett Mallory drawled. 'Anything but.'

'Then why does giving me a ride seem such an imposition? You did say that your hotel was not far from the plantation.'

'Let's just say that driving you to Shatobi might not be wise. I doubt Jim would thank me for it. And you might not either.'

'Why wouldn't I, when it's what I want?'

'Sometimes persistence isn't a good idea, Miss Leroy.'

'In this case, it is,' she assured him.

There were a few moments of silence.

'Suppose you tell me why it's so important for you to get to see Jim today?' Brett Mallory asked then.

She gave him a steady look. 'If you must know, I can't afford a hotel room and meals. Have you any idea what it costs to travel from Canada to the tip of Africa? The two flights—because you can't fly direct—took quite a bite out of my savings. And what was left went into purchasing things for the wedding and for the clothes I'll be needing in this climate.'

'I didn't mean to pry,' he said. 'Look, why don't I give you money for a room?'

Erin's head went up proudly. 'Absolutely not! I don't accept gifts.'

'Regard the money as a loan.'

'Nor do I intend to begin married life with a debt.'

'Jim is getting himself one stubborn lady.' There was a glint in Brett Mallory's eyes.

'Does that mean you'll give me a ride?' she asked.

'I have a few errands to run before I can go to Shatobi.'

'I don't mind.'

'Could be a long day,' he added.

'I don't mind that either. *Will* you give me a ride, Mr Mallory?'

'I'm still not certain it's a good idea, but yes, you can come with me,' he agreed at last.

'Thank you.' Erin, who had seen the last of her reserves disappearing after one night in a rented room, was weak with relief. 'I have three suitcases—they're in a locked room in the hotel. Will you be able to fit them into the trunk, or would you rather Jim came for them some other time?'

Brett Mallory laughed. 'In the trunk? No, I don't think so. Now, if you'd said the boot, I might have said yes.'

'The boot?' She looked at him uncomprehendingly.

'That's what we call the back of the car here. If you're going to live in Africa, Miss Leroy, you might as well start learning the lingo.'

'Good idea,' she said.

They looked at each other, and in the same moment they laughed.

When Brett Mallory had put Erin's cases in the boot— weird word, that, along with other weird ones she'd heard since leaving Canada—he opened the passenger door, and waited for her to get into the car.

Just for a moment his arm brushed against hers, and, to Erin's horror, a rush of sensation flooded her body. She closed her eyes and took a breath. By the time Brett had got into the car himself she had control of herself once more, on the surface at least.

It did not take long to leave the town. It was quite light now, and Erin, disturbingly aware of the sinuous body on the seat beside her, decided to keep her eyes away from the man, and to concentrate her attention on a countryside that was different from anything she had ever seen.

'You should see it when it's at its best,' Brett told her.

'I can't wait! This is all so tropical, Mr Mallory, and—— '

'Brett,' he said.

'Brett...' She tested the sound of it on her tongue. The name suited him, she thought. Strong, unpretentious, a little like the man himself.

'I'm Erin,' she said with a smile, forgetting her resolve not to look at him.

His gaze moved from the road. 'Erin Leroy, soon to be Erin Saunders.' Just for a moment, his eyes took on the hooded look which she did not understand. Then he turned his attention back to the road. 'What were you saying about the scenery?'

'That it's different from anything I've ever seen. Even now, bruised and battered as it is, there's a lushness I'm not used to. Do you happen to know the name of the purple shrub that covered the hotel walls?'

'Bougainvillaea. You'll see lots of that.'

'And on the way out of the city there were other shrubs.'

'Hibiscus and azaleas and frangipani.'

'Plants I've only seen in a glass-walled conservatory, and, even then, not as huge and spreading as the ones here seem to be.'

'I suppose your winters are a bit harsh for tropical plants, Erin?' Brett remarked.

She laughed. 'That's an understatement. Where I live—on a farm near Edmonton, Alberta—only the hardiest species survive. Jim found it difficult to believe that people could live in sub-zero temperatures. He couldn't picture a countryside that was covered with snow for many months of the year.'

'You won't see snow here, Erin. Will you miss that?'

'A little. I'll certainly miss the things that go with it—skiing and skating, snowmobiling with my dad, ice-fishing with my brothers.'

'Sounds as if you've given up a lot by coming here,' he remarked.

She was caught by something in his tone. 'I'm gaining more than I'm giving up,' she assured him.

'Do you think so?'

'Of course! When you decide to spend your life with a person, it's worth leaving your home and the things you enjoy. That's what marriage is all about.'

'Is it?' he said drily.

'I take it you're not married, Brett, or you wouldn't ask the question.'

'No,' he said, his tone odd, 'I'm not married.'

For a few minutes after that there was silence in the car. Erin stared out of the window, trying to quell an unusual feeling of restlessness.

'You don't like Jim very much, do you?' she blurted out at length.

'Did I say that?'

'Your manner says it for you.'

'You're making assumptions, Erin. Actually, I happen to respect Jim very much—in some ways.' And before she could make anything of that he said, 'Why don't you tell me where the two of you met?'

'At a rodeo. Jim was visiting lumber mills further west, in search of ideas he might want to try back home. He decided to side-track and take in a rodeo.'

'You were one of the cowgirls?'

Erin laughed. 'Nothing as exciting as that. I was a spectator. Jim happened to sit down beside me. He knew nothing about rodeos and asked me to explain a few of the events to him. I was fascinated by his accent, and he seemed to like mine. When the rodeo ended, he asked me to have dinner with him.'

'He proposed to you the same evening?'

Erin laughed again. 'A few days later. I suppose you could say we had a whirlwind engagement. Jim could only spend a week in Alberta, so we had to crowd our courtship into a very short space of time.'

'And you haven't seen him since then?'

'No. We've kept in touch with letters.'

'A year of letters. Did you find that a satisfactory way of getting to know your future husband?' asked Brett.

'It was, at the beginning. We'd write every week, twice and three times a week sometimes.'

He turned his head to look at her. 'You talk as if the letters are a thing of the past.'

Erin frowned. 'After a while they became less frequent. Jim didn't write as often, and his letters were shorter. I guess he's not much of a correspondent, and perhaps we'd communicated as much as we could in writing by then. We knew we wanted to be married, but it took a long time for me to save up enough to pay for my fare. I was so excited the day I was able to phone Jim and tell him I'd bought my ticket. He said he'd arrange the wedding for a few days after my arrival.'

Brett was silent. His eyes remained on the road, as if it required his full attention.

'Jim and I got to know each other well enough to understand that we belonged together,' Erin went on. 'Now we'll know each other even better. I want to tell him about my childhood, and I want to hear about his. I want to meet his friends and learn about the things that interest him. There's so much to talk about, we'll never run out of topics.'

'And when Jim is working, what will you do then, Erin?'

She looked at him, resenting the insolence she sensed in his voice, the arrogance in his expression. Brett Mallory had no love for her fiancé, that much was obvious.

'I won't be bored,' she said tightly, and turned back to the window.

For a long while after that they did not speak. The car covered the miles, and Erin kept her eyes on a countryside that was simultaneously bruised and beautiful.

Not until the car slammed to a rapid halt did she look at Brett again. Without a word to her, he had jumped out of the car and was running towards a clump of palms near the side of the road.

A few minutes later he was back, carrying a puppy that was covered in burs and mud.

'Meet Scraggles,' he said, as he got into the car.

Erin grinned. 'In name as well as in appearance.'

'And no wonder, considering he was stuck in a muddy thicket.'

'Obviously you know him,' she said.

Her eyes were on Brett's hands, which were gently stroking the puppy's unkempt fur—tanned, long-fingered hands. Unbidden came the thought that those hands caressing a woman's body would be almost unbearably exciting. It was a thought to be pushed aside a moment after it materialised.

Oblivious of the effect his stroking movements were having on Erin, Brett said, 'How the puppy managed to get where he did, I can't imagine. Scraggles belongs to some children I know, Amy and Tim Anderson. They live on a citrus farm quite a distance from here, and they'll be heartbroken that their puppy is gone.'

'I can imagine. Losing an animal is traumatic,' Erin agreed.

'Amy and Tim will be even more upset than most children. Their mother was killed in a motor accident a year ago, and they've had a hard time getting over their loss. They've become very attached to this pup. In fact, they're probably out at this moment, searching for him.'

'Lucky you saw him.'

'Yes. We'll have to take him home.'

Brett put the puppy on the back seat. Almost immediately the little creature began to whine. Looking over her shoulder, Erin saw that the puppy was shivering.

'Let me hold him,' she said.

'Didn't you notice the state he was in? If you were wearing jeans it might not be so bad, but those white trousers of yours will get grubby.'

Erin smiled. 'I don't mind.'

Still Brett hesitated. 'A dog that hasn't been house-broken yet—he might leave his calling-card.'

'That wouldn't worry me either—these trousers can be washed. Poor little thing, just listen to him cry! Give me the puppy, Brett.'

As Brett put the puppy in Erin's lap, one of his hands touched hers. Her breath jerked in her throat as she looked at him. He was waiting for her, an expression in his eyes that made her throat even tighter. He was so close to her that she saw his long lashes and the golden lights in his eyes. He leaned forward, and she saw his mouth searching for hers.

Just then the puppy moved. It was the impetus Erin needed to move herself.

'No!' she exclaimed on a shuddering breath, and snatched her hand from Brett's.

The moment was broken. Seconds later Brett had pushed the gear-stick into 'drive', and they were on their way once more.

CHAPTER TWO

TURNING off the highway, Brett drove some way along a farming road and then through a pair of stone gates. Had Erin been more in control of herself, she would have been enthralled to find herself in the middle of a citrus farm—trees bearing oranges and lemons and a mandarin-like fruit which was called a *naartjie*, as far as the eye could see. As it was, the brief encounter with Brett had left her feeling unsettled.

The car had just stopped outside the farmhouse when a jeep, approaching from a different direction, jerked to a halt, and out spilled a man and two children. The man wore a harassed look. The children, a girl and a boy, no more than four and five years old respectively, were tear-stained and dusty.

'Brett,' said the man, walking up to the car. 'We've had a bit of trauma. Scraggles is missing. Amy and Tim are beside themselves, and I just don't know where to...'

His words trailed away, his expression turning to one of pure astonishment as Erin opened the door on the passenger side of the car and got out.

'*Scraggles*?' His eyes were on the puppy in her arms.

Beside the jeep, the children stood rooted to the ground. Then they lurched themselves towards Erin.

'Scraggles! It's Scraggles!' they shouted simultaneously.

For a few minutes there was pandemonium—laughter and exclamations as the children grabbed the little dog from Erin's arms.

'We searched the whole farm,' their father said then. 'Where on earth did you find the pup, Brett?'

'On the main road. Stuck in a thicket, and looking extremely sorry for himself.'

'Thank heaven you saw him! The kids would have been distraught if something had happened. If he'd been lost, or hurt, I don't know what——' The children's father broke off once more, and now he was looking at Erin. 'I'm sorry, we're all so relieved about the puppy that I'm afraid I've forgotten my manners. Brett may have told you that our family has been through a rough time lately.'

Brett made the introductions. 'Erin Leroy—Wayne Anderson. And these two nice children are Amy and Tim.'

Erin was shaking hands with Wayne when Brett added, 'Erin is Canadian. She's come out to marry Jim Saunders.'

Wayne looked puzzled. 'I'd heard there was going to be a wedding, but I don't understand—why is Brett driving you to the plantation, Erin?'

'I arrived a day early, and it seems that Jim wouldn't have received the phone call telling him about my change of plans,' Erin explained. 'It was just fortunate that I met Brett in Nelspruit, and that he agreed to give me a ride to Shatobi.'

'The storm...' Wayne said slowly. 'I have no idea whether the phones at Shatobi are in order yet—a lot of the lines are still down—but you could try calling the plantation from here, Erin. My own phone kicked back in a few hours ago.'

Erin's eyes sparkled with mischief. 'At this stage, I think I'd prefer to keep my arrival a surprise.'

'It may be that.' Oddly, Wayne was looking at Brett.

'I do have one favour to ask of you before we leave,' Erin said. 'May I use your washroom? I'd love to change into other clothes. It's so long since I last saw Jim...'

'Of course,' Wayne said.

'I warned Erin that Scraggles's unkempt state would play havoc with her white trousers.' Brett's tone was dry.

Wayne eyed Erin ruefully. 'Amy will show you the way. Unfortunately, I think the puppy left more than mud on your clothes. Why don't you leave your things here, and I'll return them to the plantation when they've been washed?'

'I can easily wash them myself.' Erin smiled at the father of the two small children. He was very nice, she thought. He had kind eyes and a gentle mouth, and, though he was probably about the same age as Brett, grief had had the effect of making him look older.

Brett opened the boot of the car, and Erin took a change of clothing from one of her suitcases. Cuddling the puppy in her arms, Amy led the way into the house and pointed out the bathroom.

Erin splashed cold water over her face and arms before changing into a jade-coloured trouser-suit. As she combed her hair and applied a bright coral lipstick, she smiled to herself, glad that she'd had the chance to refresh herself. After more than a year apart from her fiancé, she wanted to look her best when she arrived at Shatobi.

Looking into the mirror, she tried to see her face as Jim would see it. Erin had not reached the age of twenty-two without knowing that people regarded her as appealing rather than beautiful. Her curly hair was the colour of honey, and her lips had a tilt which had tempted several men into kissing her. Her eyes were her best feature: they were deep and clear green, fringed with thick lashes. Eyes like forest pools, Jim had said, waxing poetic on the night he had proposed to her.

When she emerged from the house, she saw that Amy had rejoined her brother; they were playing with the puppy on a patch of grass near the drive. The two men stood by the jeep, talking. Erin was too far away to hear what they said, but to judge by their faces their conversation was serious. She was walking towards them when Brett looked up. He muttered something to Wayne, and the conversation halted abruptly.

Both men were watching her as she approached. Wayne's gaze was openly admiring. Brett had the assessing look which, after less than a day in his company, was becoming familiar.

'Stay a while,' Wayne invited. 'We could sit by the pool and have something cool to drink.'

'It's time we went on. Some things can't be postponed.' Brett's eyes were hard.

'Yes, well...' Wayne looked at Erin. 'I hope you'll visit us some time. I know the children would like to see you again.'

'I'd like to see them too—after the wedding,' she said, and saw the two men exchange a glance.

After leaving the Anderson farm, Brett made two more stops: once to drop off some farming implements he'd picked up for a friend; the second time to look at a horse he was thinking of buying. But at length they left the farming country and came to the forests.

Sitting forward in her seat, Erin looked with interest through the front window of the car. Wherever she looked now, she saw trees. Trees standing tall at the side of the road, covering mountains and valleys, reminding her of the foothills of the Rockies just a few hours from her home. Yet there were differences too, for now and then, amid the neatness of the forests, there would be a stretch of jungle, primitive and lush and overgrown, that would be unlike anything she had ever seen.

Brett drove in silence. Once, when Erin glanced at him, he turned and met her look, and she glimpsed an odd tension in his eyes. Dropping her gaze, she saw the tightness in the hands that held the wheel, and she remembered the looks Brett and Wayne had exchanged. She could only suppose that the two men had had a falling-out of some sort with Jim.

Her breathing quickened as Brett turned off the highway, and on to a sand road. Beneath the wheels of the car, pine needles hissed and whispered. The road was narrow, and the trees met above it in a kind of canopy.

Erin turned to Brett. 'Is this Shatobi?'

'Yes.'

'Where's the mill? And the house?'

'Not much further to the house. The mill is a mile or so further on.'

'And your hotel, Brett? Where's that?'

'A few miles further on along the main road.'

'Then we'll probably see you quite often, Jim and I.'

'You may see me sooner than you think, Erin.'

The grimness in Brett's tone had Erin puzzled. If he didn't like Jim, why didn't he just come straight out and say so? She would tell him that her loyalties would lie with her husband; that if he did not want to associate with Jim he would not be seeing much of her either. Which might be just as well, really.

They rounded a bend, and, without warning, came upon a small clearing.

'This is it,' Brett said, as the car slowed silently to a halt.

Erin stared through the window at the wooden house, which she recognised from the pictures Jim had shown her. A romantic-looking cabin, an abode for honeymooners, a place to be alone, to make love, for two people to enjoy each other's company. It was a little smaller than she had expected, but she knew from Jim's descriptions that it was comfortable.

A truck stood at the side of the house. A red Toyota was parked in front.

'This is where Jim lives,' Brett said, and again there was the hard edge to his tone.

'It's lovely.'

'A little lonely, perhaps?'

'Not at all,' Erin said firmly. Turning to Brett, she held out her right hand. 'I'm very grateful to you for the ride. Thank you so much.'

He ignored the proffered hand. 'I'll come inside with you.'

'I'd rather you didn't, Brett. I haven't seen my fiancé for more than a year, and I'd like our reunion to be private. You do understand, don't you?'

'I won't stay—unless you want me to.'

He was behaving so strangely. Did he have to have things spelled out for him?

'We'll have you over for dinner after we're married,' she said.

'Thank you,' Brett said drily. And then, 'At least let me go with you to the door.'

'No. I'd like you to leave now. I have to be alone when I see Jim—it's important to me.'

'You don't know what you're asking,' he said brusquely.

Erin looked at him tensely. 'You're beginning to frighten me, Brett. I get the feeling there's something you want to tell me—something about Jim. You've been behaving so strangely all day.'

Something flickered in the dark eyes. 'I won't come to the door if you don't want me to. But I'll remain out here a few minutes.'

'No.'

'Only until I know you're OK.'

'Anybody would think Jim was some kind of Bluebeard who was going to tie me up in his castle and never let me see daylight again!' she protested. 'We both know that's silly. Jim is a very nice man who wants to share his life with me—I wouldn't have travelled all this way if I didn't believe that. And, to judge by the two vehicles, he can't be far away. If he isn't in the cabin, I'll wait on the porch until he arrives.'

'Sometimes it isn't a good idea to go barging into things, Erin.' Brett's gaze lingered on her face.

'I'm hardly doing any barging. For heaven's sake, Jim and I are going to be married in a few days. I can't wait to see him, but I don't intend knocking on that door until you've gone.'

A look of decision came into the rugged face. 'OK, Erin, I'll go. What do you want me to do with your suitcases?'

'Leave them here, under the trees. Jim will bring them in later.'

Without another word, Brett got out of the car, lifted Erin's cases out of the boot, and put them down at the side of the road.

Erin put out her hand again. This time Brett took it, his grip warm and firm. A strange sensation quivered along her arm, unsettling her, so that she withdrew her hand quickly, just a moment too soon.

'Once more, thanks for everything,' she said brightly.

'Remember me wondering if you'd thank me?'

'I do remember, and I'm thanking you now.'

'Yes,' Brett said.

His eyes held hers for a long moment. Then he turned, got into the car, and drove noiselessly away. Only when he was out of sight did Erin walk towards the cabin.

There was no bell, so she knocked on the door. As she waited for Jim, she looked around her. Here too there were signs of the storm. Pools of water lay in depressions in the ground. Leaves and pine needles were scattered everywhere. Moss clung thickly to logs, and near the house were broken toadstools and flowers. There was a fair amount of tidying up to do in the clearing, but nothing that could not be done with a good rake and broom. Working together, she and Jim, it would not take them long to restore the clearing to its natural beauty.

Erin was smiling to herself as she knocked once more. When there was still no answer, she pushed at the door. To her surprise, it opened. Feeling a little like Goldilocks, she walked inside.

The smile left her face as she found herself in a dark, rather cluttered room. Someone had obviously made a half-hearted attempt at straightening the mess, for a pile of empty beer cans was stacked against one wall, a box of magazines against another. In the centre of the room stood a table, covered with oilcloth; around it were three unmatched chairs. A bachelor's pad in the midst of a forest, Erin told herself wryly. Well, a few cans of paint would make a difference, as would some new furniture. She would have to begin sprucing up the cabin after she and Jim were married.

From somewhere in the house came the sound of music, probably a radio. Erin was about to investigate when she heard a door open. Moments later Jim walked into the living-room—a rumpled, bleary-eyed Jim. Apart from a pair of skimpy underpants, he was naked.

They looked at each other in astonishment: Jim obviously shocked by the unexpected apparition in his living-room; Erin dismayed by the change in the man she had known only as clean, charming and boyishly handsome.

She was the first to recover. 'Honey!' She ran to him, and tried to put her arms around his neck.

But Jim took a step backwards, evading her embrace. 'Erin?'

She heard the tentativeness in his tone, as if he recognised her, but did not quite believe it could be her.

'Yes, honey, it's me.'

'What on earth are you doing here?'

She danced him a mischievous smile. 'We have a date on Saturday—remember? Oh, Jim, it's so good to see you.'

Once more she tried to step close to him. Again, he moved away.

'Jim, what's wrong? Honey, aren't you glad to see me?'

'I am ... But I don't understand—how did you get here, Erin?'

'Someone gave me a ride. Didn't you hear the car?'

'Cars don't make much sound on these roads. And the radio was playing.'

'I hoped my arrival would be a surprise,' she said flatly.

'It's some surprise, all right.' Jim did not have the look of an elated bridegroom. 'I was expecting you tomorrow.'

'You really didn't get the phone call, then?'

'Phone call?'

'Brett said you wouldn't have. That the lines were down because of the storm.'

'Brett? Brett Mallory?' Jim's lips tightened. 'Where does he come into this?'

'It was Brett who brought me here. There was a bit of a mix-up with my flights. The plane I was going to catch from London was cancelled, and I was put on an earlier flight. I asked Laura to phone and let you know. I didn't know about the storm, and the lines being down.'

'God!' Jim raked his fingers through his unkempt hair.

'I got off the train at Nelspruit, expecting to see you. Of course, you weren't there—how could you be?—but I met Brett, and I talked him into giving me a ride.'

Erin saw something like despair in her fiancé's eyes. Slowly she said, 'Brett suggested I stay over in Nelspruit, that I wait there until you came for me tomorrow.'

'That would have been better. I wish you'd listened to him,' Jim said unhappily.

'Honey, I'm sorry if I did the wrong thing, but at the time it seemed right.'

'I'm not ready for you, Erin. I was going to prepare...'

Erin's eyes swept the ramshackle room. 'We'll do things together.'

'Yes...'

'It's a little warm in here; I'd like to take off my jacket and freshen up a bit. Is the bedroom through that door?'

'*Don't* go in there!'

She stared at him in surprise. 'But, Jim——'

He seemed to be making a great effort at calmness. 'As I said, nothing is ready for you.'

'I don't care about that. Being here with you is all that's important. It doesn't matter if the bedroom is untidy.'

A look of decision appeared in Jim's eyes. 'I want you to go to the hotel for the night,' he told her.

'Why?'

'It's best that way.'

'I don't understand,' she faltered.

'Come to think of it, we shouldn't be spending the days before our wedding together anyway,' said Jim firmly. 'That's it, Erin—you'll stay at Brett's hotel until Saturday.'

Erin looked uncertainly at her fiancé. All the way from Canada she had pictured their reunion, had seen the whole thing in her mind. The happiness in Jim's face when they met. The fierceness of their embrace—for oh, what passion there had been in their kisses in that magical whirlwind time of their romance! If she had taken Brett's advice and remained in Nelspruit, her first sight of Jim would not have been so shattering. She would have been welcomed not by this sullen, unshaven man, but by the laughing young prince who had swept her off her feet a year earlier.

'Wait here,' Jim said. 'I'll be dressed in a tick, and then I'll drive you to the hotel.'

'I can't afford it,' Erin protested. 'That's why I persuaded Brett to give me a ride to Shatobi today.'

'I'll pay for you. That isn't a problem.'

'But, Jim . . . Honey . . . I'd rather stay here.'

'No,' he snapped.

'All right, then, if it means so much to you, I'll go to the hotel. But not now. I've spent a whole day in Brett

Mallory's company, when it's you I want to be with. Let's at least have a few hours together.'

'We'll come back here after we've booked you in.'

'But, Jim...'

Erin's words tailed away abruptly as a woman's voice called, 'What's keeping you, honeybun?'

Erin froze. 'Who's that?' she demanded.

Jim's expression was a little wild. 'Erin...'

The voice came again from somewhere in the house. 'Where are you, Jimmy? You sure as hell are taking a long time to bring me a beer.'

'Who *is* that, Jim?' demanded Erin.

'Nobody in particular—an acquaintance. We...we were drinking together. Wait here, Erin. I'll be right back and then I'll drive you to the hotel.'

'Are you coming, honeybun?' called the voice. 'My warm body's beginning to freeze over, waiting for you.'

'*Jim*...?'

Jim had the look of a man who wished he could transport himself instantaneously to some place far away. Neither he nor Erin moved. They stared at each other, both frozen with shock.

And again that voice. 'You really are the limit, Jimmy Saunders! Tomorrow your wretched fiancée will be here, and after that we'll have to do our loving in secret. Let's at least make the most of today. Don't keep me waiting, honeybun!'

'I'm going in there,' Erin said, her throat so dry that the words emerged with difficulty.

'*No!*'

'I have to see this—this acquaintance.'

'No, Erin, don't! Please, honey... I'll drive you to the hotel. You'll stay there until the wedding. Don't go in there, I said!'

Jim lunged at Erin as she went past him, but, with a strength born of anger and despair, she managed to evade him.

In the open doorway of the bedroom, she stopped still, stifling a gasp at sight of the near-naked woman lying on the rumpled bed.

'What the hell?' the woman exclaimed. 'Get this dame out of here, Jim!'

'Priscilla——' Jim began.

'Now! It's bad enough that your fiancée will be here tomorrow, and we won't be able to——'

'This is Erin,' Jim said, in a strangled voice.

'Is this a joke?'

The woman called Priscilla stared at Erin for one horrified second. Then she grabbed a sheet and pulled it up to her chin.

The taste of bile rose in Erin's throat. As she reeled out of the room, she had the awful feeling that she was about to throw up. Somehow she made it through the living-room and to the door of the house.

Jim was running after her. 'Erin, wait!' he called.

His hand was on her arm, but she snatched it away.

'Erin...'

'Leave me. Just leave me,' she sobbed.

'Erin...honey...'

'Leave me alone!'

'Give me a few minutes to get dressed. Dammit, Erin, I can't run out looking like this. Wait while I put on some clothes, then I'll drive you to the hotel.'

But Erin lurched blindly away from him.

At the first bend in the road, out of sight of the house, she sank on to the ground and wept. After a few minutes, she got to her feet. First she walked, then she ran. She had no idea where she was going. All she knew was that she had to put as much distance as possible between herself and Jim and that dreadful woman Priscilla.

The road was muddy in parts from the storm. Twice Erin tripped and fell. No point in running, she realised, and slowed to a walk.

For the first time she noticed that it was no longer as light as it had been. It would soon be night. Not for a moment would she consider returning to the cabin in the clearing, but she could not stay in the forests. *Where could she go?*

The hotel ... Brett had said it was situated a few miles down the main road. How many miles? Could she get there before night fell?

From somewhere behind her she heard the sound of a vehicle. It had to be Jim, coming to look for her. Quickly she threw herself to the ground behind some trees. Perhaps because her clothing was green, and it was already quite dark, Jim did not see her. He passed without stopping.

Erin began to walk with new purpose down the winding forestry road. Once more she had the sense of the trees forming a canopy overhead, but she could still make out the sky. It was growing darker all the time.

Rounding a bend, she saw paving ahead. And then cars. She was almost at the highway now.

'Erin,' someone said, then a familiar figure walked through the trees towards the road.

'Brett!' She was weak with relief. 'I didn't see you. Where's your car?'

'The road's too narrow to allow for parking, so I stopped in a clearing.'

She stared at him. 'You were waiting for me?'

'I thought you might need me.'

'You must have been very certain I'd come this way,' Erin said ruefully.

'I thought you would.'

'You knew Priscilla was in the house?' she asked.

'I guessed she might be.'

'How did you know, Brett?'

'The red Toyota's her car,' he said.

Once more Erin had a taste of bile. Finding Jim and Priscilla together had been bad enough. The thought that Brett had known all along that she would be humiliated was unbearable.

He reached out his hand to her, but she took a quick step backwards.

'Let's go to the car, Erin.'

'No.'

'Don't be an idiot.'

'You must be itching to get home, and yet you've been hiding in the trees because you knew I'd come running this way. How very gallant of you, Brett,' she said scornfully.

'You're angry with Jim, so you're letting out your feelings on me, Erin.' His lips were hard. 'And yes, you're right, I do want to get home, so let's go to the car.'

'Suppose I don't want to ride with you?'

Brett's eyes lingered on her face in the disturbing way that was becoming familiar. 'We both know you're a gutsy girl, Erin Leroy,' he said softly, 'but this isn't the time for independent action. Where do you think you'd go alone, and at this time of the day?'

She hesitated. 'You said your hotel was a few miles down the road.'

'A few being ten, and it will be dark within the hour. Apart from the fact that we're both going the same way,

Erin, wouldn't you rather have a lift with me than with Jim? You must have seen his truck zipping down the road a few minutes ago.'

'Yes...'

'You haven't told me what happened when you walked into the house, but my guess is that Jim is out looking for you. If he doesn't find you soon, he'll realise he must have missed you, and he'll be back this way.'

Erin shuddered. 'I hadn't thought of that.'

'So it's Jim or me. The choice is yours, Erin.'

'Not much of a choice, is it?' she said, and followed him to the car.

CHAPTER THREE

THE fight went out of Erin as she got into the car. As Brett walked around the vehicle to the driver's side, she covered her face with her hands. By the time Brett had got into the car, she was trying very hard to quell the fresh tears that threatened to spill out of her eyes and down her cheeks, and her breath was coming in gasps.

She was aware of Brett sitting silently beside her, and even through her unhappiness she was grateful that he had enough sensitivity to let her be. A few minutes passed, then she wiped her eyes, dropped her hands to her lap, and looked up.

'Jim just went by,' Brett said.

'Did he see us?'

'No. He's obviously out looking for you. Perhaps he thinks he missed you somewhere along the way, and decided to back-track. He must be wondering what happened to you.'

'Let him wonder.' Erin looked at Brett. 'Why didn't you warn me about Priscilla?'

'I wanted to, but I couldn't.'

'You must think me very stupid,' she said quietly.

'Innocent would be a better word.'

'And more than a little naïve?'

'A little of that too. You hadn't seen Jim for a year, his letters had become less frequent, and yet you travelled all the way from Canada with such confidence.'

'He said he loved me. We were engaged. The wedding was arranged.'

'Even so.'

Erin's throat was tight, her jaw ached. 'You must have spent the day regarding me with contempt.'

There was a glint in the dark eyes. 'Contempt, Erin? Why?'

'Because I was so trusting. So certain that Jim would arrive at the station, and afterwards at the hotel. So positive that he'd be overjoyed when I surprised him at his house.'

'Actually, I thought the man who would have earned your unconditional trust was very fortunate.' Brown eyes held green ones, defying them to look away. 'The only person I had contempt for was Jim.'

'You did drop a few hints...'

'I thought you'd have picked up on them. Didn't you wonder what they meant?'

'I did, yes. There was your reluctance to give me a ride, your warning that neither Jim nor I would thank you for it if you let me go with you. That *was* a warning, wasn't it?'

'Yes, Erin, it was. Surely you must have made something of it?' asked Brett.

'I just thought you felt it would take something away from our reunion if I wasn't at the station when Jim came to meet me. Which he'd have done tomorrow, I assume,' said Erin.

'Probably.'

'And then, later, when I saw you and Wayne talking so seriously... I knew there was something, of course, but I imagined a falling-out with Jim.'

'We were wondering if we should say something to you, if we should stop you from going to the plantation.'

'Why didn't you, Brett?' she demanded.

'It didn't seem the right thing to do.'

'Jim's dirty laundry, not yours.'

The dark eyes were steady and direct. 'Something like that. You can look daggers at me all you like, Erin, but think of it—if I had told you about Priscilla, would you have believed me?'

'I might have.'

'I don't think so. Loving Jim, trusting him as you did, I think you'd have imagined I had some ulterior motive for telling you about his mistress. Besides which, Wayne and I both thought that Jim should tell you himself.'

Erin closed her eyes. Behind her lids she saw once again the picture of the near-naked woman on the bed. The brazen look on her face, and the stricken expression in Jim's eyes. She could taste once more the foulness in her mouth.

She found she could not look at Brett. 'When we got to the house...you knew she'd be there with Jim.'

'Her car was there—it wasn't hard to guess.'

'You insisted on going to the door with me. When I said no to that, you wanted to wait until I was inside.'

'Erin...' he began.

'To pick up the shattered pieces, Brett?'

'To be there for you,' he said quietly.

'You should have told me then. Maybe you couldn't tell me before, but you should have told me then.'

'I couldn't do it. And when you've had some time to reflect, you'll know that's true.'

'What did you think it would do to me to see Jim and Priscilla together?' she demanded.

'I realised you'd be hurt, Erin. I'd have given everything I had to spare you that hurt, but I knew you wouldn't believe what I had to say.'

'You could have tried.'

'I did—within limits,' he pointed out.

'You didn't go far enough. I feel ... I don't even know how to tell you how I feel. Angry. Shattered. Devastated.'

'You'll get over it,' he said, touching her hand.

Erin snatched her hand away, as if she'd been burned with a hot coal.

'*Will* I get over it? Is that something else you know? Are you always so certain of your facts, Brett?'

'I really am sorry you had to be hurt,' he said, with a gentleness she hadn't expected.

'That's why you waited for me here. You knew I'd come stumbling down the road, bawling my eyes out like some wretched soap-opera character. And there you'd be, Brett Mallory, strong, macho, ready to mop up the tears.'

'Don't do this to yourself, Erin,' Brett said gently.

She put her hands in front of her face again. Her shoulders heaved.

After a while she looked up. The branches of the trees were indistinct now against the growing darkness of the sky.

'It was awful,' she said.

'I don't imagine it was pleasant.'

'It was much worse than you realise. They'd been making love.'

'My God! You caught them at it?'

'Not quite, though a few minutes earlier or later and I'd have walked in on them. As it was, Jim was going for some beer. He had very little on, just a pair of underpants.'

'He must have been shocked to see you.'

'Does the English vocabulary contain a stronger word than "shock"? He couldn't believe I was there, in his house. He tried to get me to leave, said he wasn't ready for me. He wanted to take me to your hotel. We were talking when Priscilla called to him. Something about her warm body needing him, about the necessity of making love before his wretched fiancée arrived and they'd have to start meeting in secret.'

Brett looked disbelieving. 'She said all that?'

'She didn't know I was there. I had to see her. Jim tried to stop me, of course, but I managed to get to the bedroom. And there was Priscilla, almost naked and in bed.'

Erin felt very cold suddenly. An iciness gripped her. It started deep within her, and spread through her body. She began to tremble once more, quite violently this time.

'Erin...'

In a rapid movement, Brett slid across the seat and put his arms around her. For a second or two Erin sat quite still. Then she pulled away.

'Don't touch me!' she snapped.

'You're in shock.'

'I'll get over it—you said so yourself.'

Brett's arms tightened around her. They were hard and strong, arms that would make a woman feel wanted and secure—in normal circumstances. But nothing would ever be normal for Erin again.

She pushed at him with her hands. 'Leave me alone!'

'I'm not trying to hurt you. I want to comfort you. To tell you that I'm sorry for what happened.'

'You don't understand, Brett—I don't want to be touched.'

She opened the door and was about to get out of the car. Then she remembered that she had nowhere to go, and she remained in her seat. Brett's arm was still around her shoulders.

'I don't want to be touched!' she said again, fiercely this time. 'Not by you, not by any man. I feel dirty, degraded.'

'You've no reason to feel that way, Erin. You did nothing wrong.'

'I was a fool,' she muttered.

'But not a villain.'

'I feel dirty, all the same.'

Brett withdrew his arm and moved away from her. For some reason, even with the physical contact broken, something of his warmth still lingered on her skin.

'What now?' he asked.

'I'll go back home. To Canada.'

'There's not much you can do right now.'

'I have to get away from this place,' she insisted.

'I could drive you to Nelspruit, but what would you do there at this time of the day? Come to the hotel with me, at least for tonight.'

Erin thought about that. Although all she wanted was to get as far away as she could from the plantation, there was some sense in Brett's suggestion. She could not begin to plan her return home until tomorrow.

'I was going to walk to the hotel,' she said, on a shuddering breath.

'Don't you think a lift with me is a better alternative?'

'I expect you're right.'

For the first time since her abrupt departure from Jim's cabin, Erin's voice held the ghost of a smile.

The headlights of the car lit up a sign which proclaimed the entrance to the hotel: Hilltop Inn. As Brett turned off the main road, Erin wondered if she would have noticed the sign in the dark.

'I've just thought of something,' she said, as they drew up outside a lovely, rustic-looking building, and a dog came bounding up to the car. 'I've no idea of your tariff.'

'If there's a vacancy—and I have reason to believe there will be—there won't be a charge.'

'That's very generous of you,' Erin said stiffly, 'but I can't possibly accept the offer.'

'Why not?'

'I was naïve once. I won't be again.'

A derisive look came into Brett's face. 'Think I'll expect payment in kind?'

'If you did, you wouldn't receive it,' she assured him.

'Thanks for the warning.'

Erin felt her face go hot, and was glad that it was too dark for Brett to see the colour in her cheeks.

'I got into trouble because I was too trusting,' she said unsteadily. 'On the way here, I made myself a promise that I would never make that mistake again.'

'I'm not Jim,' Brett said.

'That's true. But Jim seemed honest and open. I had no reason not to trust him. That being the case, I can't trust anybody else from now on.'

'You had one bad experience, and so now you're going to make another mistake by over-reacting.'

'Over-reacting?' she echoed.

'I offer you a room, and you assume that I'm after your body,' Brett explained.

'Isn't that the only thing men want from a woman?'

'In the space of half an hour you've become cynical, Erin.'

She lifted her head. 'That's right,' she said hardily.

Without warning, Brett reached out and touched her face. His hand was warm, making her feel vital and alive, stirring a longing deep inside her. It was a longing she had no intention of acknowledging, even to herself. She stiffened, then pushed his hand away.

'So now you're a cynic, Erin. I think I preferred the eager, enthusiastic girl I got to know earlier, even if she did make mistakes,' Brett said softly.

'Forget her. She doesn't exist any more.' Erin's voice shook.

Brett sat back, his long legs stretched out in front of him, an arm extended the length of the seat.

'All right,' he said, 'I won't deny that I'd like very much to make love to you, but I'm not about to force myself on you. I've never forced myself on any woman—that isn't my style. I've offered you a room, no compensation asked—neither in money nor in kind. Do you want it?'

A pulse throbbed in Erin's throat. She realised she had no alternative but to put her trust in Brett, at least for tonight.

Before she could speak, he turned and gripped her hands in both of his. 'Well?' he demanded.

The contact sent a charge of electricity through her wrists and up her arms. She jerked her hands out of his.

'I told you not to touch me!' she snapped.

'And I may as well tell you that I'm losing all patience with you. I'm not a rapist, so don't treat me like one.' His voice had gone cold. 'I'm late, I should have been here long ago. Do you want the room, or shall I take you back to Jim? If you like, I can dump you on the road or in the forests. Whatever your choice, it's time you made up your mind.'

'I don't really have a choice, do I?' Erin whispered. 'I'll take the room. And tomorrow I'll see about getting back to Canada.'

'As you like,' Brett said, his tone oddly flat.

A little belatedly, Erin added, 'Thank you.'

They left the car and walked into the hotel together. The reception area was inviting, with a few lovely posters, a clay urn holding proteas and dried grasses, and a bookcase filled with books which guests could borrow to read during their visit.

The receptionist was red-haired, freckled and pretty. 'Good to see you back, Brett,' she said, with a welcoming smile. 'We expected you hours ago. We were even beginning to wonder whether you'd missed your train.'

'I was delayed, Liz,' Brett said, with a brief look at Erin.

'I suppose you know that the telephone lines are down?'

'I do. I tried to let you know when I was coming, but of course there was no getting through. Any word when the phones will be repaired?'

Liz grimaced. 'They're working on the lines—that's as much as we've been told. It's been a little difficult, with people being unable to make reservations.'

'Do we have any vacancies tonight?'

The receptionist threw Erin a curious look. 'Nine and eleven are free. The people who were to have taken them didn't turn up. It's possible they tried to cancel, but couldn't get through to us.'

'I see. This is Erin Leroy, Liz. She'll be taking eleven tonight. Will you see about checking her in?'

Brett riffled quickly through the mail that had accumulated in his absence, while Erin filled in the hotel register. When she put down her pen, he said, 'I'll see you to your room.' He looked at the receptionist. 'See you a little later, Liz. Then you can fill me in on what's happened while I was away.'

Erin followed Brett out of the main building and down a path lined with shrubs. On either side of the path were round cottages with thatched roofs—'rondavels', Brett called them. A few were in darkness, but most had lights shining in the windows. Stars were beginning to dot the sky, and the air was sweet with a mixture of heady perfumes.

Brett turned off the path and stopped at one of the rondavels. He turned a key in the lock, and reached out to switch on a light.

'I hope you'll be comfortable here,' he said, as he followed Erin inside.

'Comfortable!' she exclaimed, looking around her. 'Compared with what I saw of Jim's cottage, this is a palace!'

She had an impression of restful charm, but it was a vague impression only, for there was something else that filled the room—a sensuous maleness that emanated from the man who seemed to dominate his surroundings with the force of his vitality.

'I wouldn't have minded living in Jim's cabin,' she said, a little awkwardly. 'It was an awful mess, but I'd have fixed it up and made it habitable. If Jim and I . . . If things had been different, I'd have enjoyed doing that.'

'I think you would have.'

Erin was glad when Brett took a step towards the door.

'I'll leave you now,' he said. 'I'll be back later.'

'I can cope on my own now,' she said quickly.

'You can also carry the independence thing a bit too far. You've barely eaten all day, Erin. Apart from a few sandwiches when I stopped to look at the horse, you've had nothing. What did you intend to do about dinner?'

'I hadn't thought about it.'

'I'll pick you up in an hour or so, and we'll eat together.'

'I'm not really hungry...' she began.

'You can watch me eat, in that case,' he said unsympathetically.

Brett was at the door when Erin exclaimed, 'My suit-cases! I forgot all about them. When I dashed out of Jim's cabin, they were still under the trees.'

Brett frowned. 'I didn't think of them either.'

'I don't think I can face going back to the cabin to pick them up,' she confessed.

'You won't have to—I'll fetch them for you in the morning. I'm sure Liz won't mind lending you whatever you need until then.'

'Brett...' Erin stopped.

'Well?'

'Thank you. You've been very kind.'

'For a man,' he said, but she saw that he was grinning. He leaned towards her, his hand cupping her chin. Erin forced herself not to react; she just stood very still.

'A cliché,' Brett said softly, 'but things may seem better in the morning.'

When Brett had left the rondavel, Erin sat down on the bed. Suddenly she felt drained. So much had happened in the last few hours, yet until this moment events and emotions had kept her going. For the first time she realised that, apart from being unhappy, she was also tired, hungry and hot. She had left Canada in the midst of a long, cold winter, with the thermometer showing a reading far below zero. Just a few days later she was on another continent, in another hemisphere, in another season. Even now, in the early evening, the temperature had to be well in the nineties.

She got up from the bed, opened a door, and found herself in a pretty bathroom. The shower looked inviting. She longed for her luggage and a change of clothes, but at least there was a robe behind the door. She would shower, then relax for a while in the robe before putting on the jade trouser-suit once more for dinner with Brett.

She stood for a long time beneath the shower, enjoying the water and the perfumed soap. She washed her hair, and when she had towelled herself dry she put on the robe and returned to the bedroom. In seconds she was asleep on the bed.

The sound of knocking woke her. She opened her eyes, and for a few moments looked around her, bewildered. The room was in darkness, but a light shone in the bathroom, shedding its glow through the open door. Erin saw a second bed, a dressing-table, curtains that were vaguely familiar, and suddenly she knew where she was.

The knocking sounded again. Brett... He must have arrived to pick her up for dinner. She looked down at herself, unwilling to let him see her in the robe. Another knock, more insistent this time. She would have to open the door, tell him she'd fallen asleep, and ask him to give her a few minutes to get ready.

Opening the door a crack, she said, 'I'm sorry, Brett, I dozed off and——'

'We have to talk.' A man's voice, but not Brett.

'*Jim?*' she gasped.

'Open the door, Erin.'

'I don't want to see you,' she hissed through the crack. '*Please.*'

She caught the note of despair in his voice. 'I'm not dressed, Jim. All I have on is a robe.'

'I won't touch you,' he promised.

'Why would you, when you've done all the touching you want today?' she snapped.

'For God's sake, Erin! That remark was unnecessary. Are you going to let me in?'

'All right,' she agreed, 'but only for a few minutes.'

She wrapped the robe tightly around herself. Then she switched on the light, opened the door and stepped backwards as Jim entered the room.

He didn't look much different from the man she'd surprised in the cabin earlier. True, he was wearing jeans, shirt and shoes now, but his appearance was tousled and unkempt, as if he'd forgotten to bath or shave or brush his hair that day. His eyes were red-rimmed and his cheeks were flushed.

'I've been looking for you ever since you left,' he said.

Erin didn't care for the accusing tone in his voice. 'Really?' she said coldly.

'I went out in the truck and drove down the forestry road. I was certain I'd see you. When I got to the highway I was puzzled. I couldn't believe you'd have walked so far in the time, and I wasn't sure which way to go from there. I drove a few miles one way, then the other. Eventually I turned back. I thought perhaps I'd passed you on the road, and not seen you.'

'That's exactly what happened,' she told him.

'Where were you?'

'In the trees.'

'You could have walked into the road. I'd have seen you then.'

Erin lifted her head. 'Did it occur to you that I might not have wanted to see you at that moment?'

Jim looked embarrassed. 'I realise you were surprised when you walked in and found Priscilla——'

'Surprised, Jim? The word doesn't begin to describe what I felt.'

'Erin——'

'When I ran out of your house, all I knew was that I had to get away. I had no idea where I was going, what I was going to do.'

'You certainly found a solution quickly,' he said drily.

'That was because Brett was waiting for me. He'd parked his car in a clearing.'

'Knowing you'd go running that way, of course,' Jim said truculently.

'Yes.'

'He'd seen Priscilla's car, I suppose.'

'Actually, he'd been throwing me warning hints all day,' said Erin. 'A little too subtly, as it turned out, because I didn't understand what he was getting at. He didn't want to give me a ride to Shatobi. He thought I should spend the night in Nelspruit—but I already told you all that.'

'Was it Brett's idea to bring you to the hotel?' asked Jim.

'Yes, though I'd have come here in any case, even if it had meant ten miles on foot. How did you know I was here, Jim?'

'I didn't. I took a chance. After I'd been up and down the forestry road a few times, I was reaching the end of my tether. I didn't know if you'd been attacked, or if you'd got lost somewhere. You're a stranger here, Erin, and you don't know the surroundings. And then Priscilla suggested I try the hotel.'

Erin gave a harsh laugh. 'Nice of her.'

'Come on, Erin...' Jim said stiffly.

'Did you see Brett? Did he tell you where to find me?'

'Do you think he'd have told me? I went to Reception and asked Liz.'

'I see,' she said flatly.

'Look, Erin, I'm sorry about what happened, I really am. I never meant to hurt you. But you have to realise, I wasn't expecting you. I had no idea you were coming a day sooner than planned.'

'Am I supposed to *apologise* for my early arrival?' she demanded.

'Not exactly. But I was hoping you'd understand...'

'Understand what, Jim? The fact that my fiancé was making love to another woman?'

Jim reddened. 'We're not married, Erin. Not yet.'

'What's that supposed to mean?'

He was unable to meet her eyes. 'The way I see it, commitment doesn't begin until after the marriage ceremony.'

Erin stared at him incredulously. 'You're saying it was fine for you to carry on an affair until our wedding? Because that's what you and Priscilla have been having, isn't it, Jim? And going back some time, obviously, because both Brett and Wayne Anderson seemed to know about it.'

Jim shifted his feet on the carpet. 'It looks bad, I know.'

'Yes, it does.'

'But if you really thought about it you'd know how it happened. We've been apart a year, Erin. A year's a long time for a man to be alone.'

Looking at Jim now, Erin found it difficult to remember the man she had fallen in love with after the rodeo. He had been so handsome then, so full of life and laughter and charm, sweeping her off her feet with his kisses, his endearments and his compliments.

'I was lonely too, Jim,' she said slowly.

'It isn't the same for a woman.'

'Isn't it?'

'Besides, I wouldn't have minded if you'd had a few friends,' he added.

'Friends, Jim, or lovers?'

He was silent, his lips clenched in a jaw which, Erin saw for the first time, could have been stronger.

'You once said we belonged together, Jim.'

'I meant it. I gave you a ring, didn't I?'

'Yes, you did, and I wore it until a few minutes ago. It's on the bedside table now.'

'You can put it back on,' he told her.

'No.'

'Because of Priscilla?'

'I'm surprised you have the nerve to ask the question,' Erin snapped.

'You wouldn't have known about her if you'd arrived a day later.'

'I guess not,' she agreed.

'I'd have met you at the station. We'd have had a slap-up meal at a nice restaurant in town. And then we'd have come back to the plantation. I had everything planned.'

'Thoughtful of you!'

He shot her a suspicious look, as if he was uncertain whether or not she was being sarcastic.

'I had the whole wedding planned, Erin—flowers, drinks, a party here at the hotel, honeymoon in Durban.'

'When were you going to tell me about Priscilla?' she asked directly.

Jim pushed his hand through his hair. Erin saw that he could not meet her eyes.

'I don't think you'd have told me about her at all,' she told him.

'Erin...'

'*Would* you, Jim?'

'I'm not sure... Perhaps there'd have been nothing to tell you by then.'

'You're not saying that you and Priscilla were going to end your affair today?'

Jim hesitated a moment. 'We might have.'

'You forget, *honeybun*, I heard what Priscilla was saying before she realised I was in the house. The affair was going to continue after we were married, but in secret.'

Jim looked unhappy. 'I'll end it,' he told her.

'Don't bother.'

'I'll tell Priscilla that I can't see her any more.'

'You don't have to do that.'

Jim's face was flushed once more, his expression defiant. 'What are you trying to tell me, Erin?'

'I'd have thought you knew,' she said. 'There isn't going to be a wedding, Jim.'

An odd look came and went in his eyes. Relief, Erin thought, yet something like defeat as well.

'I told you,' he said, 'it's all arranged.'

'That's too bad.' Erin went to the bedside table, picked up the engagement ring she had worn with such pride, and put it in Jim's hand. 'Take this.'

Jim looked down at the ring. When he looked up once more, his expression was shamefaced. 'People make mistakes, Erin,' he muttered.

'Maybe they do, but this is one mistake I can't live with. Especially not when I know that you'd go on seeing Priscilla after the wedding.'

'I told you I'll end it,' Jim insisted.

'Against your will.'

Once again he was silent. Erin saw that he was struggling with his feelings, wondering whether to admit the truth, or to say the things he thought she wanted to hear.

It hurt to ask the question, but she had to ask it nevertheless. 'Are you in love with her, Jim?'

'Erin, don't.'

'I have to know.' Her voice throbbed with emotion.

'I...I'm very fond of her.'

'Oh, God, Jim,' she muttered.

'I was in love with you. I wouldn't have asked you to marry me if I hadn't loved you.'

'And then you met Priscilla, and everything changed.' It was painful to say the words.

'I'm sorry...'

'How long has it been going on?' Erin asked directly.

'Erin...'

'How long, Jim? Did it start about the time your letters tailed off?'

'About then,' he admitted. 'I didn't mean it to happen, Erin. We met at a dance, we got on well that night, and things just went on from there.'

'You should have told me,' she said.

'I wanted to. I thought of it many times, but in the end I couldn't.'

'Why not?'

'Your letters were filled with such excitement. You were sewing your dress, saving for the journey. If I'd told you I'd changed my mind about the wedding, you'd have been disappointed.'

Erin wondered if Jim had any idea of the pain his words caused her. Trying to keep her tone even, she said, 'I'd have got over it—I'd have had to, wouldn't I? However hard it would have been to accept a broken engagement, in Canada, with my family around me, it would have been a hundred times easier than here, where I know nobody.'

Nobody but Brett. She pushed him from her mind.

'You let me travel all this way, Jim, knowing that we were going to go through a farce of a marriage, that you were going to make vows that you had no intention of keeping. Knowing that you'd be unhappy and that I—when I eventually found out about the affair—would be devastated.'

'I don't know what to say,' he muttered.

'There's nothing you can say. Not any more.'

'What will you do now, Erin?'

'I've had no time to think.'

'You'll go back to Canada?'

'There's not much else I can do.'

This time the expression in his eyes was unmistakable. He was relieved at the fact that Erin would vanish from his life.

'I brought your luggage,' he said. 'I put it in the truck on the off chance I'd find you.'

'Thanks.'

'I'll fetch it from the truck and bring it into the rondavel.'

'Leave it outside,' she said flatly. 'I never want to see you again, Jim.'

'Erin...'

'Go,' she said, her voice choked. 'Go now!'

In the doorway, Jim turned back. His mouth opened, as if he was about to speak. Erin closed the door in his face, before the words could leave his lips.

CHAPTER FOUR

WHEN Erin had closed the door, she leaned back against it. In Jim's presence she had managed to preserve some measure of control, but now her breath was coming in heaving gasps. She could hear the sounds his footsteps made on the path; he was walking quickly, loudly, as if he was very angry. As if his pride had been hurt rather than his heart, came the wry thought. He was walking away with Erin's hopes and dreams, with the pictures she'd stored in her mind.

Beside her bed in Canada there had been a photo of Jim and herself, arms around each other's waists, smiling into each other's faces, Jim looking jauntily handsome in a T-shirt he had bought at the rodeo and a baseball cap belonging to one of Erin's brothers perched at a slant on his head. On Erin's dressing-table had been other photos, ones which she had taken of Jim alone, and which she had had enlarged. There was also the picture Jim had sent her of the house in the forest—her future home.

After her engagement ring, Erin's photos had been her most cherished possessions. Not a day had gone by when she had not looked at them; they had kept her spirits high when it had seemed as if she would never accumulate enough money to pay for her journey to Africa; as if she would never see her fiancé again.

Erin had brought the photos with her. Most of them were in her suitcases, but her favourite photo, the one of Jim and her together, was in her bag. Leaving the door, she opened her bag and took out the photo, a little ragged at the edges from the many times she had looked at it. Her fingers clenched on it convulsively. Then, with a little sob, she began to rip it up, quickly, savagely, the pieces dropping as she went.

When there was nothing left to rip, she looked at the tiny bits of paper scattered on the carpet—the shredded pieces of a dream—then she lurched on to the bed and broke into frantic weeping.

She did not hear the sound of scraping as Jim deposited her suitcases outside the rondavel, did not hear the door open, then close again hastily. She was oblivious to everything but her grief.

She recoiled when a hand touched her hair.

'*No*, Jim!' she exclaimed.

'I'm not Jim,' someone said quietly.

Erin turned her head slightly on the pillow. 'Brett...?'

'Yes.'

'Leave me alone,' she ordered jerkily. Her eyes were swollen, her throat was raw, and it was an effort to speak.

'I'm not leaving you,' he said.

'Please...'

'You don't really want to be alone now, do you?'

'I must look a mess,' she sobbed.

Brett laughed softly. 'Does it matter?'

Without waiting for an answer, he sat down on the bed and gathered her into his arms. Erin hated him to see her cry, but, as if she had no control over her tears, they continued unabated.

'I can't help it,' she sobbed once.

'I know.'

Brett held her close, her face against his chest, stroking her hair, apparently uncaring of the tears that dampened his shirt.

Gradually Erin's weeping lessened.

'I'm sorry,' she said, when she could speak.

'For what?'

'For losing control.'

'You're human, aren't you?' he said quietly.

'I guess so . . .'

She was quiet again, and Brett did not speak either. For the first time, Erin became aware of things she had not noticed until then: the hardness of Brett's chest against her cheek, and the way it rose and fell with his breathing. The strong heartbeat. A smell in her nostrils that was unmistakably masculine; clean, yet virile and exciting.

Aware of sensations that she had never experienced before, not even with Jim, she moved restlessly in Brett's arms.

'I'm fine now,' she said.

'Good.'

'You can leave me now, Brett.'

'Not yet, Erin.'

She tilted her head so that she could look at him. The light caught his hair, giving it a glossy sheen. His jaw was broad, and so strong that above it his mobile lips looked unexpectedly sensuous. Beneath thick brows and long lashes, his eyes were unreadable.

Unsteadily, Erin said, 'Jim was here.'

'I know.'

'When he knocked on the door, I thought it was you. If I'd dreamed it was Jim, I wouldn't have answered the door.'

'Did you talk?' asked Brett.

She swallowed. 'At length.'

'Perhaps it's just as well.'

'If you think that talking made me feel better about what happened today, you're mistaken, Brett. If anything, I feel worse.'

'I still think it's good you had a chance to talk.'

Erin was quiet a moment. 'How did you know he was here?' she asked then.

'Liz mentioned it. He left your luggage outside the door.'

'He said he would,' she said flatly.

'I brought your cases inside.'

'I didn't hear you.'

He brushed her cheek with his hand. The feel of his hand against her damp skin was so good. *Too* good. Abruptly, Erin pushed herself away from Brett and sat upright.

He reached for her left hand. Holding it firmly in his, he said, 'You're not wearing your ring.'

'I gave it back to him. The wedding is off.'

Something flickered in the dark eyes. 'Oh?'

'You couldn't have thought I'd go through with it?' she countered.

'You travelled a long way so that you could share your life with Jim. Women do forgive their men sometimes, Erin.'

'Not this woman.' She pulled her hand out of his. 'Jim still thought we'd be married. Can you believe it? He even offered to end his affair with Priscilla.'

'And you said no?'

'Absolutely! I could never trust him after what happened. Do you know that he was actually put out because I arrived a day early and caught him with Priscilla? He didn't seem to see anything wrong with what he was doing. As far as Jim is concerned, commitment only begins after the wedding.'

Brett was silent a moment. Then he said, 'You'll get over it.'

'Words,' Erin dismissed bitterly.

'Maybe. Yet I believe you'll find happiness again.'

She felt tears starting once more. 'It's never nice to be jilted, but if Jim had written to me about Priscilla and broken off our engagement I wouldn't have travelled halfway across the world for nothing.'

'Erin——'

'How could he start an affair with that woman when he was engaged to someone else? Obviously he made no secret of their relationship, because you knew about it, and so did Wayne.'

'I don't condone what he did,' Brett said slowly, 'but a year is a long time for a man like Jim to be without a woman.'

'He said that too,' Erin admitted.

'People do find themselves attracted to others, no matter how well-intentioned they are.' There was a provocative note in Brett's tone now. 'You should know that, Erin.'

She felt herself tensing. 'I never once went out with a man all the time Jim and I were engaged.'

'There's been something between the two of us since the moment we met,' he went on relentlessly.

'*No*!' she whispered.

'Admit it, Erin. Admit that you felt something when we were in the car together.'

'No!'

'Admit that if you hadn't been on your way to your fiancé you'd have let me kiss you.'

'I wish you wouldn't say these things!' she said furiously.

'Why are you so angry? Because I'm too close to the truth?'

Erin stood up abruptly. 'Even if what you said was true—*if*, mind you—I would never have acted on my feelings. There was never a moment when I wasn't clear about my commitment to Jim. I would never—*never*, Brett!—have let another man into my life.'

'Never is one of those words that are difficult to say, Erin, because you can't be sure about them.'

'But I am sure. I'm positive. Just as I'm positive that there'll never be another man in my life after this.'

'Because you'll always be in love with Jim?' Brett was watching her intently.

'Because I'll take care never to let myself be hurt again.'

'What about love, Erin?' Brett asked quietly.

'It won't have a place in my life.'

'I hope you don't mean that.'

His eyes were on her face, lingering, quite deliberately, on her lips. Erin trembled as she saw his gaze descend, resting for a moment on her throat before travelling along her body.

'Don't look at me like that,' she whispered.

'I can't help it—you're looking very sexy.'

Catching the direction of his eyes, Erin glanced down at herself. To her horror, she saw that the opening of the robe had parted. She could see her breasts, and knew that Brett saw them too. Roughly she tugged the robe closed.

'Come here,' he said huskily.

'No.'

She jerked as Brett caught her free hand and pulled her towards him. He was still sitting on the bed. She tried to get away from him, but at that moment he stood up and drew her against him.

She had not realised quite how tall he was until their bodies touched. She was not small, yet her head was on a level with his shoulders.

It should have been easy enough to escape his kisses, but, as he cupped her face with his hands and tilted it upwards, she found herself unable to move away. His lips came down on hers, quite lightly, but with a sensuousness that sent the blood racing through her body. She tried to resist when she felt his tongue at her lips, but, as if in response to an inner yearning that was stronger than the directives of her conscious mind, her own lips parted. Brett's kisses became deeper and more passionate, drugging kisses, so that for a while Erin did not think about Jim and the cabin and what she had found there. The only reality was Brett: his hands on her face, his lips, the tongue that sent such primal sensations flooding through her.

His arms were around her body now, drawing her closer against him. And suddenly she was kissing him back, kiss for kiss, unthinking, uncaring of anything but the sweetness of what was happening to her.

Brett was the first to draw back. Lifting his head, he took a ragged breath, then looked down at her.

'What did I tell you?' he asked huskily. 'You can't shut men out of your life, Erin.'

His tone did not impact on her as much as his words. Eyes dazed with shock, she stared up at him. A flush spread over her face as she understood what had happened, and that she had done nothing to prevent it.

'You said you'd never force yourself on me,' she accused.

'I didn't. You were every bit as involved as I was, Erin.'

Her heart was pounding so hard that she wondered if he could hear it. Inside her there was a trembling which she tried very hard to suppress.

He gripped her shoulders with his hands. 'You can't deny any longer that there's something between us.'

'I can't deny that I kissed you.' She threw the words at him. 'But any other man would have had the same response from me tonight.'

Brett's gaze narrowed. 'What are you trying to say?'

'You caught me off guard, Brett,' she said mockingly. 'Think of it—a woman who'd just been rejected by the man she was about to marry.'

'So?'

'I believe you were trying to prove something to me with your kisses. Didn't it occur to you that maybe I was trying to prove something too?'

Brett looked at her for a long moment, his eyes hard. 'What was that?' he demanded roughly.

'That I wasn't totally undesirable. You caught me on the rebound, Brett. My response meant no more than that.'

'Is that what you've decided to tell yourself?' he asked drily.

'It's the way it is. What else could it be when I was in love with Jim until today?'

They stood looking at each other a few seconds longer. Erin's face was still flushed, her breathing too ragged. After a moment Brett shrugged. Slowly, unhurriedly, he moved away from the bed.

He was at the door when he said, 'You have twenty minutes to get dressed.'

'Dressed for what?'

'Dinner. We'd arranged to eat together, remember?'

'After what just happened?' she queried.

'You still have to eat.'

Obviously, the intensity of their kisses had meant nothing to him. The knowledge caused Erin a pain that she could not deny, and did not want to understand.

She shook her head. 'I don't think so.'

Brett's grin was both unexpected and wicked. 'I'll be in the dining-room in twenty minutes. It's in the main building. If you decide to join me, Liz will direct you.'

'I haven't said I'll come.'

'The choice is yours,' he said, and left the room.

Erin was tempted to forgo dinner. The thought of eating with Brett was more than she could bear.

He had left her luggage near the door. She knew which suitcase she wanted, and lifted it on to the second bed. There was no point in unpacking, not when she was going to leave Hilltop Inn in the morning, but she needed her toiletries and another change of clothes.

Although it was not long since she had showered, the unaccustomed heat was so enervating that she stood under the water again. Then she took from her suitcase the first garment which met her eye. As it happened, it was one of her favourites, a yellow dress with black dots, a wide black belt and huge black buttons. She brushed her hair, then applied a light foundation, a dusting of green eyeshadow and some lipstick.

When that was done, she looked at her watch. A little after eight o'clock, she registered with a sense of disbelief. Her body-clock, only just beginning to adapt to the time difference between Africa and North America, was set in the morning. Despite the sleepless night on the train, and the trauma of the hours that had followed, she was not ready for bed. She had nothing to read, nothing to sew. Evidently Hilltop Inn was a place for people who liked their holidays free of all urban disturbances, for there was not even a TV in the room. Normally content with her own company, Erin was restless; she had no idea how she could pass the evening.

Brett had been right about one thing—she was hungry. Far too hungry to wait until the morning for her next meal. A quick look in the mirror, then she left the room and took the dark path to the main building.

At the reception desk, Liz looked up with a friendly smile. 'Hello, Erin, looking for the dining-room? Brett asked me to tell you the way when you came along. It's down the passage, first door to the right.'

'Thanks,' Erin said.

A little grimly, she followed the receptionist's directions. The dining-room was easy to find. She saw Brett immediately, sitting alone at a table in a corner of the room.

As Erin approached him, he looked up with a wicked grin. 'Glad to see you decided not to stand on your pride.'

Arms folded, she stood by his table. 'You knew I'd come. Didn't you? Liz didn't seem at all surprised to see me.'

'I didn't take you for an idiot. Why don't you unclench your arms and sit down?'

After a moment, she did just that. Brett put a menu in front of her. 'Take a look at this,' he said. 'A waiter will come for your order.'

The menu was short but interesting. Conscious of a growing hunger, Erin hesitated over her choice.

'Nothing you fancy?' Brett asked.

'Every dish sounds delicious. I wish I had time to sample them all.'

'You could,' he told her.

'Not if I leave here tomorrow.'

'You don't need to do that,' said Brett.

'I have to go to Nelspruit in the morning,' Erin insisted.

'You could also stay here a while.'

Caught by an odd inflexion in his tone, Erin looked up. The gaze that rested on her face was infinitely disturbing. Remembering the sensations she had experienced when they'd kissed, she moved restlessly in her seat.

'Since there's nothing to keep me here, the sooner I leave the better,' she said unsteadily.

'I don't agree—but the decision has to be yours, Erin.'

'Yes...'

His eyes held hers for a long moment. She was the first to move her gaze.

'Meanwhile,' Brett said smoothly, 'if the menu selection is too overwhelming, I can vouch for the *filet mignon*. The chef's a wizard with beef.'

'Sounds great,' Erin agreed.

'Perhaps you should take up my other suggestion with the same alacrity.'

'I can't,' she said, 'I really do have to go home.' And then, 'Brett...'

'Yes, Erin?'

'One favour. I'm starving, and I'd like to enjoy my dinner. Can we leave Jim and Priscilla and the wedding out of our conversation?'

'Agreed,' he said, with the kind of smile which, in normal circumstances, might have found its target in her heart.

The waiter arrived at that moment. When Erin had given her order, she looked around her with pleasure. The dining-room was lovely—rustic, with lots of light-coloured wood and wicker and colours that made one think of the outdoors.

'This is beautiful,' she said.

'Thank you,' smiled Brett.

'Have you been here long, Brett?'

'I was born not far from here, on a plantation not unlike Shatobi. Timber was never my line, but hotels fascinated me. I was in my late teens when my father died and my mother moved to the coast. I could have moved away too, but by then I'd decided to build my own hotel, and this seemed the obvious place for it.'

Erin looked at him incredulously. 'You achieved all this when you were a teenager?'

His smile was attractive. 'I started with two rather crude rondavels. The rest evolved bit by bit, growing whenever I had money and ideas.'

His confidence was attractive too; it was evident in every aspect of the man—his vital voice, his lithe movements, the strong face and body, the eyes and lips that creased so easily into laughter. It would be too easy to become prey to Brett's magnetism—more difficult to forget him—which made it all the more important that Erin leave here the next day.

With the limits of their conversation defined, they talked easily after that. Brett had never visited Canada, and his questions were many. As Erin talked about places and activities she knew and loved, she relaxed for the first time since leaving Jim's cabin. She was unaware that her eyes sparkled and her face grew animated as she talked. She did not know that her expression was rapt when Brett spoke in turn.

She was astonished when she looked around her, and saw that she and Brett were the only ones left in the room. She glanced at her watch, then at Brett. 'It's after ten-thirty. I'd no idea it was so late.'

'We don't have to end the evening,' he said.

'Yes,' she said, very firmly, 'we do.'

The look he threw her was provocative. 'If you say so.'

With studied calmness, she said, 'I'd like to make an early start tomorrow. How do I get to Nelspruit from here, Brett? Is there a bus?'

'I'll give you a lift. What will you do when you get to town, Erin?'

'Find a travel agency and make plans to fly home.'

'A woman who knows her mind.'

His tone was so brisk that Erin felt deflated.

They left the dining-room together. Erin said she could make her own way to her rondavel, but Brett said he had to walk that way anyway.

Outside the door, they stopped.

'Thanks for a good evening,' Erin said politely.

Brett laughed softly. 'Such formality. You forget I held you in my arms while you wept.'

'I don't want to think about that,' she said quickly.

'I know I agreed not to talk about Jim and Priscilla and all the rest of the mess, but I do have one question, Erin.'

She looked up at him, tall and strong and uncompromisingly male. He was grinning down at her, but something in his eyes made her heart thud hard against her chest.

'Did you think of Jim tonight?'

Erin hesitated a moment. 'Not as much as I thought I would,' she said then, honestly.

'I'm glad.'

Brett bent his head, and before she could stop him his lips touched hers, quite briefly. The kiss was over before she could push him away.

Moments later he had vanished from sight in the darkness.

When Erin woke the next morning, the dim light of dawn filled the room. For a few seconds there was the bewilderment she had felt on being roused from her nap the previous day. Then she recognised the rustic furnishings of the rondavel.

Glancing at her watch, she saw that it was still early. Too early to go and find Brett.

When she had dressed, she opened the door and went outside. Later it would be hot, but it was chillier now than she had anticipated. She went back for a sweater, then set out along the path she had seen only at night.

Grass and shrubs, wet with dew, brushed at her shoes and jeans. The other rondavels had a closed look, and when she came to the main building that looked closed too, as if guests and staff had not yet woken to the new day.

Erin walked further, absorbing a garden and a view that she had not seen the previous day. The grounds of the hotel were even bigger and more beautiful than she had imagined. Rondavels were situated on either side of the main building. A little distance away were tennis courts, a bowling green and a kidney-shaped swimming-pool, its water opaque in the early morning light. Here and there, in the gardens, were groupings of garden chairs, all with a panoramic view over tree-covered mountain slopes. And everywhere there were flowers and shrubs, brightly coloured, sweet-smelling, tropical, rampant.

When Erin had explored the gardens, she took a path that led to the side of the hotel. The still air carried the sounds of neighing and the stamping of hoofs.

Rounding a bend, she arrived at the stables. She had always loved horses, and was about to go closer when she stopped suddenly in her tracks.

A man was saddling a horse. Concentrating on what he was doing, he had not seen her walking along the sandy path. Faded jeans moulded powerful legs, and a T-shirt clung to a chest that was all hard muscle. He reminded Erin of a cowboy, his superb body ready to pit itself against the power of a furious steer. Watching him, so at ease with himself and his horse, so utterly sexy, Erin felt her heart do a little somersault in her chest.

Becoming aware, suddenly, that he was not alone, he turned his head.

'Why, Erin!'

'Hi, Brett.'

'I thought you'd be sound asleep at this hour. Everyone else is.'

Not wanting him to know how deeply he affected her, she made herself throw him a smile. 'Like you, I'm an early riser. I've been exploring. Do you mind?'

'Feel free to go wherever you like,' he told her.

'I can see why you decided to build the hotel in this place, Brett,' said Erin. 'I've been wandering through the gardens. All those shrubs—they're so beautiful.'

'Nice, aren't they?'

'They're amazing!' She laughed up at him, the sound of her laughter bell-like on the still air. 'Remember me telling you yesterday that the only tropical plants I've seen were in a glass-walled conservatory? And pint-sized in comparison with the stuff you have here. I keep stopping to look and feel and smell. I wish I knew the names of all your shrubs and flowers.'

'If you gave yourself some time before rushing off back to Canada, you could get to know them all.'

The laughter left her face. 'I need to talk to you, Brett,' she said shortly.

'Oh?'

'I'm glad I found you here.'

'Well?' There was an odd look in his eyes.

'Brett——'

He did not let her finish. 'Do you ride, Erin?' he asked.

'Yes, of course, but——'

'Why don't I saddle a horse for you?'

'I don't think you heard me, Brett. I need to talk.'

'I did hear you,' he said, his expression enigmatic. 'I was going out myself when you appeared. There's a place I know where we can talk.'

Riding with Brett was not what Erin had had in mind this morning, but as she looked at him, six feet two inches of magnificent male, temptation was a quickening in her veins.

She fought the emotion. 'We can talk here.'

Brett's grin was maddening. 'I know how you feel about men in general, but why do yourself out of some pleasure, Erin? You might regret passing up on the ride when you're back in those icy wastes you were describing to me yesterday.'

Temptation got the better of her. 'OK,' she said.

Erin watched as Brett finished saddling first one horse, then began to work on another. Everything about him bespoke toughness and strength. The horses were quiet, as if they understood his authority and respected it.

Fascinated, Erin watched him as he worked, her gaze drawn to his hands as if they were magnets, defying her to look elsewhere, her senses quickening as she remembered the feel of those hands on her own body.

He turned, so suddenly that there was no time to mask her expression.

His eyes raked her face. 'Well?' he asked, after a moment.

'I'm ready, Brett.'

'Are you?' His tone was insolent now.

She felt herself redden. 'To ride,' she said, a little too quickly.

'Ah . . . to ride.'

'As if you thought I meant anything else!' Tension made her voice brittle.

'Actually,' Brett drawled, 'women have told me, in just that tone, that they wanted me to make love to them.'

'I'd have thought it was clear I wasn't one of those women,' Erin said through dry lips.

'Really?'

'Just because I was rejected by my fiancé doesn't mean I'm looking for some other man to take his place.'

'You might enjoy going to bed with me,' he suggested.

'Knowing that I'd only be hurt again, I would loathe every second,' she assured him.

'I've told you a few times that not every man is like Jim.'

'I'm in no mood for comparisons.'

Angrily Erin strode away from Brett. She hadn't taken more than a few steps when he was beside her, one hand touching her arm, the other holding the reins of the smaller horse.

'What about our ride, Erin?' he asked.

'I've changed my mind.'

'You wanted to talk.'

'That's right...'

'This is your horse.'

'Let's talk here, Brett.'

'No.' The authority in his tone defied argument. 'We'll ride, Erin. Trust me—you'll feel better for it.'

The previous day, on the way from Nelspruit to Shatobi, Erin had watched the countryside from the road. On horseback, everything looked different. Even at dawn, and with the damage left by the storm, the scenery was beautiful.

Side by side, they made their way along a trail that was not unlike the forestry road which Erin had stumbled along after leaving Jim's cabin. They had been riding for some time when, without warning, they left the orderliness of the pine forests and were in jungle-like terrain, where moss clung thickly to rocks and tree-stumps, and the air had a dank, dark odour. And then, as suddenly as they had entered the jungle, they left it once more. They were on another trail now, clear of trees, yet narrow, and following the upward curve of a mountain slope.

Brett was riding ahead of Erin now. For a few minutes her eyes were on the broad shoulders, the proud thrust of the head, the body that sat so easily in the saddle, and then, firmly, she moved her gaze and tried to concentrate on the scenery once more.

The trail became steeper, but the horses, accustomed to the mountainous paths, managed it well. Twenty minutes further up the slope, Brett reined in and turned his head.

'We can give the horses a rest now,' he said.

Erin was puzzled. There was only some rough ground on either side of the trail—nothing to suggest that they had arrived anywhere in particular.

'This is it?' she asked disbelievingly.

She saw the laughter in Brett's eyes. 'Meaning you don't want to dismount?'

Erin shrugged. If this was where Brett wanted to talk, that was fine with her.

In a lithe movement, he vaulted from his horse. When he had tethered it loosely to a tree, he came over to her.

'I can manage,' she said, a little breathless as she saw him reaching for her.

'I know you can, prairie girl.' His teeth were white and strong in the lean, tanned face. 'I can help you all the same, can't I?'

His hands were on her waist as she began to dismount. Erin had spent much of her life on horseback, in the company of a father and brothers who expected her to look after herself. The hands which lifted her from the horse, steadying her as her feet touched the ground, were a new experience.

For a long moment they stood beside the horse, Brett's hands still on Erin's waist, his long, hard body so close to hers that she felt as if she knew every inch of it.

It was Brett who broke the closeness. Taking the reins of her horse, he led it to a tree. As she watched him tether it, Erin was aware of an irrational disappointment. This time, however, when he turned his head she made sure that her own expression was controlled. She treated him to a cool smile as he walked towards her, a smile that concealed emotions she did not even want to try to understand.

'This way,' Brett said.

Silently, Erin followed him, walking away from the trail over rough ground. The ground grew even rougher. Stones skittered underfoot, and, without warning, Brett reached for her hand. She tried to pull away, but his grip was firm.

'There...' he said, seconds later.

Erin gasped. Such was the shape of the slope that until that moment she had had no idea of where they were going. She could not have guessed that the land would fall away from the mountain in a kind of precipice. She stood quite still, drinking in the panorama below her.

Later in the day, the valleys and the mountain slopes would be green, but now they were misted.

'Well?' Brett asked.

His hand was still holding hers, and she made no attempt to loosen his hold.

'Fantastic!' she sighed.

'Glad you came?'

'Oh, yes!' She looked up at him with shining eyes. 'I'd also have liked to see this view with the sun shining on it. The different greens must be gorgeous.'

'They are,' he agreed.

'As it is, I'll have to try and imagine them.'

'Nothing to stop from you coming again, Erin.'

'You know that's not so.' The light had left her eyes.

'You're still set on going, then?' His voice was a little flat.

'Yes.'

'Back to Canada, as quickly as you can get there.'

'Not to Canada,' she said. 'At least, not yet. That's what I wanted to talk to you about.'

CHAPTER FIVE

'WHAT are you saying, Erin?' Brett's eyes were alert, yet, strangely, not surprised.

'I wasn't thinking too clearly yesterday,' she explained. 'All I knew then was that I had to get away from Jim, and that meant going back home.'

'And today?'

'Reality has returned. Actually, it hit me with a bit of a bang some time during the night. I suddenly remembered what I'd forgotten in my despair. When I came here, I spent all the money I'd saved.'

'Ah.'

She looked at him. 'You're not at all surprised, are you, Brett? You remembered that I couldn't afford to wait for Jim in Nelspruit, and that I wasn't certain if I had enough money to pay for my room here last night.'

His expression was hard to read. 'You paid for a one-way trip, I presume?'

'Of course. Return tickets would have been an admission of failure before the marriage had even begun.'

'You're the kind of woman who would have taken her vows seriously. "Till death us do part" would have meant just that.'

'That's right,' Erin said, restless under his eyes. She looked away from him, down over the misty patchwork of valleys. 'So here I am, unattached, disillusioned— and stony broke. I can't afford to go home.'

'Well,' Brett said, in a voice that made Erin think he was not sorry for her at all.

'Don't you see my predicament, Brett?' she urged.

'Clearly. Have you made any new decisions, Erin?'

'Two. The first, that I must return home—because I *will* get there, somehow or other. The second, that I have to find work quickly, so that I can earn enough money to travel.'

'I see.'

'Something with decent pay, because the two flights—one to Europe, and the other to Canada—cost a lot. That was why I wanted to talk to you, Brett. Do you think I should find a job in Nelspruit, or would it be better if I went to one of the big cities—Cape Town or Durban or Johannesburg?'

'What would you do there?' he asked.

'Ideally, I'd like to be a pastry chef in a bakery or a restaurant.'

'A pastry chef?' Brett looked intrigued.

'It's what I trained to do, and I'm good at it. If I can't find work baking, I could always put in time in a store—I've had quite a bit of sales experience.'

'A woman of varied skills.'

'Enough to land a job?'

'Certainly enough to land one at Hilltop Inn.'

She stared at him in astonishment. 'You're not suggesting I stay *here*?'

'Think of it, Erin. If you went elsewhere, you'd have to pay rent. You'd need money for food and transport. And those are just the basics. With what you'd have left—if there *was* anything left—how long would it take you to save up enough to pay for two major flights?'

'Months,' she said, feeling a little ill.

'That's being optimistic. With costs being what they are today, it could take you a few years.'

'That would be awful,' she whispered.

'I've just given you another option,' he reminded her.

'Not one I can consider.'

'Why not?'

Her head went up proudly. 'I don't accept charity.'

'Is that what I offered?'

'Isn't it?' she demanded.

'No, Erin. And I think I made it clear yesterday that I don't expect repayment in kind, so let's not get into that again either.'

He was so close to her, on the edge of the slope, that she could sense the warmth of his skin even though their bodies—except for their hands—were not touching. His fingers, long and hard, were interlaced with hers, and when he exhaled she felt his breath on her hair.

'What *are* you offering me, Brett?' she asked, her eyes searching his face.

'I'm a businessman, Erin. I'm always looking for ways to expand the hotel—ways of making the place more appealing for my guests. A few years ago I built the stables. Last year I added a tennis court. Next year, perhaps, I might put down a second bowling green. Lately, I've been thinking about a means of selling items produced by the local farming wives. Tourists are often keen to buy home-made jams and vegetables.'

Erin's eyes widened in astonishment. 'You want me to run a store for you?'

'Right. I'd pay you the going rate, of course. There's a rondavel that's not being used at the moment, so you wouldn't have to worry about rent. And I don't charge my staff for food.'

'It sounds very tempting,' she said slowly.

'You could make extra money out of anything you make yourself. Since you're an expert at baking, why not consider a constant stock of home-made biscuits?

Perhaps you could learn to make chocolates—they're always in demand.'

Her eyes sparkled. 'It just so happens that home-made chocolates are my speciality.'

'Are they good?' asked Brett.

'The best you've ever seen or eaten—at the risk of sounding immodest.'

'I predict you'll sell truck-loads of them.'

'Maybe...' Suddenly Erin's voice had turned half-hearted.

'I sense some hesitation. Don't you like the idea?'

'I do, very much, except for one thing.' The light had left her face.

'Which is?'

'Hilltop Inn is too close to Shatobi. You said yesterday that Jim comes to the hotel often. He won't stay away just because I'm there.'

'Make your point, Erin.'

'Imagine what it would be like for me to have to see him,' she said.

Brett's eyes were hooded. 'Are you still in love with him?'

'I feel humiliated and hurt and very angry. Those feelings aren't going to vanish overnight.'

'You haven't answered my question. Are you still in love with Jim, Erin?'

'I'm not sure... The fact is, I'd be embarrassed to face him.'

'Why?' Brett's tone was crisp. 'If anyone should be embarrassed, that person should be Jim.'

'You're right, I know, but it doesn't change the way I feel.'

There was a hard look in his face now. 'I expected more of you, Erin. You're a spunky woman. You left your home and your family and travelled halfway around the world to share your life with a man you barely knew. You were so excited, so confident when I met you yesterday. Surely you're not going to let a bum like Jim Saunders intimidate you now?'

Tears started in Erin's eyes, but she blinked them away. 'Do you think it would be easy to face the man who'd jilted you?' she demanded.

'I said nothing about easy. The fact is, I think you could do it. Don't let Jim keep you from doing what you want to do.'

'You despise me, don't you?' Erin's voice was low. For some reason, the thought of Brett's contempt hurt even more than Jim's cheating.

'Is that what you think I feel for you?' he asked, his tone sounding so odd.

She looked at him. The dark eyes were steady, yet unnerving. She found she could not hold their gaze for more than a few seconds.

There were a few moments of silence.

'I suppose you're right,' she said then. 'It's not my fault that Jim took up with Priscilla.'

'Meaning?'

'That I really do make the best chocolates.'

Brett laughed. 'There's the spunk I saw yesterday! Do I take it we're in business together, Erin?'

'I'd like that very much,' she said.

His hands cupped her face, holding it for a few seconds before sliding to her shoulders. Deciding to accept the touch as the friendly sealing of an agreement, Erin made no attempt to withdraw. Even through her sweater she could feel the strength of his fingers. She forced herself to stand very still, trying to ignore the tremors his touch provoked.

'Erin...' he said, his voice husky, then his head began to move downwards.

Erin moved her mouth sideways, beyond the reach of lips that were a little too tempting.

'I won't let you down,' she said unsteadily. 'I promise I'll make a success of the store.'

Brett did not answer, but she saw a glint in his eyes in the moment before they left the slope. When he dropped her hand, the warmth of his fingers was like a brand that had been left on her skin.

Erin's muscles felt tight as she joined Brett at the trees where the horses had been tethered. He was whistling softly to himself. If the few minutes at the edge of the slope had meant anything to him, there was nothing to show it.

He grinned at her as he tossed her the reins of her horse. Expert horsewoman that she was, she jumped lithely into the saddle before he could offer his help.

Silently they made their way down the mountain. It was lighter now than when they had climbed the slope. The trees and the wild flowers had lost their greyness, and were beginning to assume their normal lush colours. The sky was cloudless, holding the promise of a perfect day.

They returned to the hotel almost two hours after they had left it. There was activity everywhere now. In the pool, a couple were swimming, having a race, to judge by the determined pace of their strokes. On the tennis court, a doubles game was in progress. A waiter was carrying a breakfast tray to one of the rondavels, and, in the stables, a groom was putting out fresh hay.

When Erin and Brett had unsaddled their horses, they walked together towards the front of the hotel.

'Hungry?' Brett asked. It was the first personal word he'd spoken since Erin had avoided his kiss.

'Yes.'

'After breakfast, I'll take you to the rondavel I was telling you about earlier.'

'I thought you might have had second thoughts about wanting me here.' The words emerged before she could stop them.

The grin he gave her was pure devilment. 'You'll learn that I'm a fighter, Erin. When I want something—and I do—I don't give up easily.'

Brett carried Erin's suitcases to the spare rondavel. She asked him what he wanted her to do that day, and he said she could investigate the kitchen, think about how the store should be set up, and decide what she needed in the way of supplies.

'Don't get too busy, though,' he advised. 'In a day or two we'll make a tour of the district. We'll consider what we can purchase and from whom. In the meantime, why don't you just explore the hotel and have a bit of a holiday?'

When he had left the rondavel, Erin began to unpack. After almost a week in suitcases, many of her clothes were creased. Carefully she laid them out on her bed, smoothing down sweaters, putting skirts and trousers on hangers which she carried to the bathroom. She ran a hot shower for a while: if she hung her clothes on the rail for a day or two, the steam would take care of most of the creases, and the rest she would iron out later.

When she had finished putting away her things, she left the rondavel and walked to the main building. In the gleaming modern kitchen, she was met by an imperious chef who was suspicious of her reasons for wanting to explore his domain. Only when Erin had reassured him that the work she would be doing there would not threaten his meal preparations in any way did he unbend. As unobtrusively as possible, she took a mental inventory of those utensils already existing in the kitchen, and considered what else she would need.

Afterwards she strolled through those parts of the main building which she had not yet seen. Besides the dining-room, there was a card-room, a billiard-room, and a lovely lounge with a picture-window view over the pool.

At the reception desk, Liz looked up from her work with a smile.

'Hello, Erin. Brett just mentioned that you're going to be working here for a while. 'I'm really glad about that.'

Warming to the other girl's friendly manner, Erin smiled back. 'Thank you.'

'It'll be really nice to have someone to talk to.'

'Nice for me too, Liz.'

Erin was still smiling as she left the building. She was a sociable girl, and friendship was important to her. It was reassuring to know that she had made a friend at Hilltop Inn. Someone apart from Brett Mallory, whom she could not quite think of as a friend.

On Saturday morning, Erin opened her eyes with a feeling of sadness. She was to have been married today. In her cupboard was the wedding dress she had sewn with such care. In a box, as far out of reach as she could push it on the top shelf, were her veil and shoes and the ornaments she'd made for the wedding cake.

She forced herself to get out of bed, for if she stayed there she would weep, and she did not want to do that; she had wept more than enough since her arrival in

Africa. The trick was to keep busy if she was to get through the day without breaking down. The store and the baking were still in the future, but there were other things she could do.

Ten minutes after waking, she was in the pool. When she had swum fifteen lengths quickly and without stopping, she felt better. From the pool she went to the stables, where she helped the groom with the horses. Once, feeling tears form in her eyes, she leaned her face against a horse's velvety flank. By the time the groom looked up to see what she was doing, Erin had managed to blink the tears away.

Brett joined her at the breakfast table. He knew as well as she did the significance of the day, but perhaps he had decided to take his cue from her—when Erin did not mention the wedding, he didn't either.

Breakfast over, Erin asked Liz if she could help her at Reception, and Liz, who was trying to cope with an unusually hectic weekend, accepted the offer gratefully.

Erin was answering a long-distance call when it occurred to her that her parents would probably phone her that day at Shatobi. In seconds she made the decision to get in her own call first. She would tell Brett about it when she saw him, and he could deduct the cost from her salary.

'Sweetheart!' Her mother's happy voice came through the line. 'Dad and I were looking at the time. We were just about to phone you and Jim.'

'Mom...' Erin swallowed hard. Then, cutting off her mother's congratulations, and without giving more than the most pertinent details, she said that the wedding was off.

'Erin!' Her mother sounded upset. 'Darling, I'm so sorry. Come home.'

'I will, Mom, just as soon as I've saved up enough to pay for my flight.'

'How will you do that, Erin?'

'I have a job at a hotel. It's called Hilltop Inn. The owner has been very kind to me, and I'm sure I'll be happy here.'

Erin's fingers were shaking as she put down the phone. With the sound of her mother's voice still in her ears, the distance between her family and herself seemed greater than ever.

When she went to her rondavel to change her clothes in the late afternoon, she realised that only a few hours remained of the day she had been dreading. By dint of forced business and sheer determination, she had managed not to brood about what might have been. She would survive the remainder of the day just as well.

Standing before her open cupboard, she wondered what she should wear. Every Saturday evening there was a dance at Hilltop Inn. According to Liz, it was attended not only by the hotel guests but also by the local populace, who liked to dress up for the occasion.

Erin settled for a dress which she had bought in Edmonton shortly before her departure—a wisp of a dress, backless and made of a soft, diaphanous material. A perfect dress for a honeymoon, she had thought when she'd bought it; all the way home from the mall she had pictured Jim's pleasure when he saw her wearing it. But she would not let herself think about that, she decided firmly, as she clipped on matching earrings, then left the rondavel.

The dance was held in the dining-room, where the tables had been rearranged to make room for a sprung dance-floor. There was also a dais for the disc jockey who drove to the hotel every weekend.

Liz was sitting at a table with a farmer by the name of Don. When she saw Erin standing in the doorway, she waved her over and invited her to join them. Erin smiled as her new friend performed the introductions. Liz had told her all about Don—the two were unofficially engaged and planned to get married at Christmas.

In the friendly company of Liz and Don, Erin managed to push all thoughts of the wedding from her mind. People had begun to dance to the disc jockey's lively music. Some faces were already familiar to Erin—hotel guests whom she had seen in the dining-room, at the tennis courts and in the pool. Others were strangers, locals who seemed well acquainted with one another.

Erin was tapping her feet to the music when her smile froze suddenly on her face and her body went rigid. Jim had walked into the room. A cleaned-up Jim, shaved and combed and nattily dressed, the man who had rushed her through a whirlwind courtship a year earlier. Holding his hand was a woman with long blonde hair and vivid make-up; the only other time Erin had seen her, she had been almost naked.

'Hell!' exclaimed Liz, in an undertone. 'Doesn't he have some nerve!'

'I should have guessed they'd be here. I don't know why I didn't.' Erin's voice shook.

Jim spotted her just seconds after she had seen him, and Erin saw him stiffen. For a long moment their eyes met and held. Jim's gaze was the first to shift away. He muttered something to Priscilla. Then, leaving the woman standing, he strode across the room towards Erin.

'Hello,' he said, sounding awkward.

'Hi, Jim.' Erin managed to keep her own voice cool and controlled.

Jim glanced at Liz and Don, then back at Erin. 'Can we talk?'

The receptionist lifted her eyebrows at Erin in a way that seemed to say 'courage', then she and Don left the table and walked on to the dance-floor.

Jim looked uncomfortable. 'I'd no idea you were still here, Erin,' he muttered.

'Where did you think I'd be?'

'On your way back to Canada.'

'Just like that?'

'You said the wedding was off.'

'I did say that, didn't I?' she agreed.

He looked at her, his expression a mixture of trepidation and truculence. 'Are you saying you've changed your mind?'

'Bit late for that, isn't it? The wedding was to have been today. We should have been celebrating at this moment.'

'We could set another date, Erin.'

'If I answered yes to that, would you really stop seeing that woman you're with?' she asked coolly.

Jim hesitated a moment, then his head went up defiantly. 'I was always prepared to do the honourable thing—you can't say anything to the contrary, Erin. I'd have married you, you know that. I never once considered going back on our engagement.'

'Noble of you.'

'I can do without your sarcasm,' he said angrily. 'I wasn't the one who backed out of the wedding. *You* did—because you couldn't stomach a little harmless fun *before* marriage. As if I was already your property before the knot was tied.'

'I guess you could say we have different standards,' Erin said evenly. 'But we've been over all that before, so this discussion is getting us nowhere.'

'*Have* you changed your mind about the wedding, Erin?' he insisted.

'No, of course not.'

Jim's relief was so obvious that Erin did not know whether to feel amused or insulted.

'When are you leaving here?' he asked.

'I'm not—for the moment, anyway.'

'Why not, Erin?' he demanded.

'I have my reasons,' she said quietly, deciding that if Jim had forgotten her financial status she would not remind him of it.

'That's ridiculous!' He was looking distinctly put out. 'There's nothing for you here. You'll be bored in a week.'

'I don't think so. Brett has offered me a job.'

'Brett again,' Jim said bitterly. 'Hasn't the man interfered enough? If he hadn't...' He stopped.

'If he hadn't brought me to your house a day early, I'd never have known about Priscilla,' Erin finished for him.

'You wouldn't have been hurt.'

Erin remained silent.

'Look,' Jim said, with the crooked, boyish smile that she had once thought so endearing, 'I've already told you how sorry I am about what happened. I'd even be prepared to marry you, if that was what you wanted. But, since you don't want it, why don't you say no to Brett's job and go elsewhere?'

'In other words, you want to be rid of me.'

The smile vanished from Jim's lips. It had never made it to his eyes in the first place, Erin had noticed.

'In terms of people, this isn't a big place,' he said. 'We'll keep running into each other. You'll be embarrassed every time we meet.'

'No, Jim, *you* will be embarrassed,' Erin said quietly. She looked across the room where the blonde woman was watching them, her expression hostile. 'Or should I say you *and* Priscilla? Because you're obviously a pair.'

'Change your mind,' he pleaded. 'Go and live somewhere else.'

'I intend to stay where I am,' she said, very distinctly. Somehow she had managed to maintain an outward appearance of calm throughout the conversation. But the shock that had awaited her in her fiancé's cabin was still so recent that the calmness had been an act. As Jim strode away, his eyes furious, his expression frustrated, Erin was shaking. Alone in her rondavel, she might have wept. As it was, surrounded by people, she could only blink furiously at the tears that threatened to spill from her eyes.

Jim joined Priscilla, who had secured a table by this time. He sat down, summoned a waiter, and minutes later two beers were put down before them. Priscilla sipped her beer slowly, Jim downed his so fast that Erin felt sure he could not have tasted it.

Slamming his glass down on the table, he looked towards Erin, his face mutinous. A second later he jumped to his feet, pulled Priscilla from her chair, and led her to the dance-floor.

Erin tried not to watch them, yet almost of their own volition her eyes kept going to the handsome young man who had wooed her with such determination. His smile, not much in evidence tonight, was what had drawn her to him at first; that, and the adoring expression in his eyes when he had looked at her. When he had asked her to leave her home and her family, there had been some sadness, but no sense of sacrifice. She and Jim belonged together, it had been as simple as that.

A familiar voice said, 'Care to dance, Erin?'

She lifted her head to look at Brett, but her throat was so thick with tears that she could not speak. He stood by her chair, taller than Jim, his lean face rugged rather than handsome. A muscle moved in his throat, then he was holding out his hands to her.

'Come,' he said, softly this time.

She was trembling as she took his hand and got to her feet. Blindly she followed him on to the dance-floor and went into his arms. She was glad that the music was slow, so that she could stay close to him, and that the tears which refused to stay in her eyes were hidden against his shirt.

By the time the music quickened, and people were dancing without touching, Erin had control of herself once more—outwardly, at least. The dance-floor was not big. Jim and Priscilla were still dancing, and it was impossible not to see them. Once Priscilla and Erin came face to face, and for a long moment their eyes met.

All Erin had seen of the woman that other time had been a half-naked body in a rumpled bed. Looking at her now, she realised that Priscilla was very pretty. Her hair was a golden colour, straight and thick. Her eyes were a deep shade of blue and her figure seemed to curve in all the right places. She was attractive in an obvious way, she was also naturally sexy. Erin guessed that she could never have competed successfully with Priscilla for Jim's affections, even if she had wanted to.

The music began to slow once more. Priscilla threw Erin a loaded look, then she smiled suggestively up at Jim and snuggled against him. Pain filled Erin as she saw her erstwhile fiancé's arms close so tightly around the sexy woman that the two bodies seemed wedged together as if they were only one.

Coinciding with the altered mood of the music, the lights over the dance-floor dimmed. Erin had a sudden need to be close to another person. To make Jim jealous, or to shut out her feelings of loneliness? She did not question the reason, she only knew that she had to be close to Brett.

But Brett was holding her in the manner of an acquaintance rather than a lover. At any other time Erin might have appreciated that reserve on the part of a man she barely knew. Not tonight. With a movement that had nothing to do with thought, that was born purely out of despair, she wound her arms around his waist. She heard his breath, a hiss against her hair, then his arms folded around her body, and he was drawing her against him.

Now they too were dancing as one; the tall, hard body and the smaller, softer one seeming to fit together in all the right places. Erin felt Brett's lips move in her hair, and she tightened her arms around his waist. She had danced with Jim in that long-ago time which did not seem quite real now, but that dancing had been nothing like this. Brett's body had a tautness which Erin, on some level of her being, acknowledged as intensely exciting, but she did not think about that now. There was just the merciful closeness of a man who seemed to find her attractive, and on this particular evening that was all-important.

The song came to an end. There was more music, one piece leading into another, all of it slow now, for that was what people seemed to want. Jim and Priscilla, lost in each other's arms, did not move from the dance-floor.

Erin and Brett, in their own embrace, went on dancing too.

Unexpectedly, the music quickened, and seconds later the lights over the dance-floor brightened too. Brett's arms loosened their hold. Eyes dazed, Erin looked up at him.

'Feel like going outside for a while?' he asked softly.

Erin had been long enough at the dance. 'I'd like that,' she said.

The sky was cloudless in a way that it had not been since Erin had arrived at Hilltop Inn. A crescent moon and a myriad stars cast a glow over the garden. The hot air throbbed with the sound of crickets.

Erin was acquiescent when Brett took her hand. The hard fingers folded around hers, giving her a sense of safety—Brett would not let her slip in the dark. It also gave her a sense of being cared about, which was very nice after Jim's blatant behaviour.

Near the pool, they stopped. For a few minutes they stood by the water, phosphorescent beneath the starry sky. Then they walked further.

At one end of the pool was a wooden chair, wide and deep. In the daytime there would be other chairs here too, but they had been stored away for the night. Erin guessed that a solitary guest had brought out the chair in the early evening, and had forgotten to put it away again later.

'Let's sit,' Brett suggested.

'Will you bring out another chair?'

'This one is big enough for two,' he said.

With which he sat down, and, his hand still holding hers, he drew her on to his lap.

★★★★★★ PLAY ★★★★★★
£600,000 LOTTO!

★★★★★★★★★★★★★★★★★★★

NO COST... NO OBLIGATION...

NO PURCHASE NECESSARY!

IT'S FUN

IT'S FREE

**FREE BOOKS!
CASH PRIZES!**

LOTTO PRIZE DRAW
RULES AND REGULATIONS

NO PURCHASE OR OBLIGATION NECESSARY TO ENTER THE PRIZE DRAW

1 To enter the Prize Draw and join our Reader Service, follow the directions published. The method of entry may vary. For eligibility, Prize Draw entries must be received no later than 31st March 1994. No liability is assumed for printing errors, lost, late or misdirected entries and unreadable entries. Mechanically reproduced entries are null and void.

2 Whether you join our Reader Service or not your prize draw numbers will be compared against a list of randomly, pre-selected prize winning numbers to determine prize winners. In the event that all prizes are not claimed via the return of prize winning numbers, random draws will be held from among all other entries received to award unclaimed prizes. These prizes are in addition to any free gifts that may be offered.

3 Prize winners will be determined no later than 30th May 1994. Selection of the winning numbers and random draws are under the supervision of D. L. Blair Inc., an independent judging organization whose decisions are final. One prize only to a family or organisation. No substitution will be made for any prize, except as offered. Taxes and duties on all prizes are the sole responsibility of winners. Winners will be notified by mail. The chances of winning are determined by the number of entries distributed and received.

4 This Prize Draw is open to residents of the United Kingdom, U.S.A., Canada, France, Germany and Eire; 18 years of age or older except employees and their immediate family members of Torstar Corporation, D. L. Blair Inc., their affiliates, subsidiaries, and all other agencies, entities, and persons connected with the use, marketing or conduct of this Prize Draw. All applicable laws and regulations apply.

5 Winners of major prizes will be obligated to sign and return an affidavit of eligibility and release of liability within 30 days of notification. In the event of non-compliance within this time period, prizes may be awarded to alternative winners. Any prize or prize notification returned as undeliverable, will result in the awarding of that prize to an alternative winner. By acceptance of their prize, winners consent to the use of their names, photographs or other likenesses for the purposes of advertising, trade and promotion on behalf of Torstar Corporation, without further compensation, unless prohibited by law.

6 This Prize Draw is presented by Torstar Corporation, its subsidiaries, and affiliates in conjunction with book, merchandise and/or product offerings. Prizes are as follows:-

Grand Prize - £600.000 (payable at £20,000 a year for 30 years).

The First through to the Sixth Prizes may be presented in different creative executions, each with the following approximate values:

First Prize		- £25,000
Second Prize		- £ 6,000
Third Prize	(x 2)	- £ 3,000 each
Fourth Prize	(x 5)	- £ 600 each
Fifth Prize	(x 10)	- £ 150 each
Sixth Prize	(x 1,000)	- £ 60 each

7 Prize winners will have the opportunity of selecting any alternative prize offered for that level. Torstar Corporation may present this Prize Draw utilizing names other than 'Million Dollar Sweepstakes'.

For a current list of prize options offered and all names that Prize Draws may utilise, send a stamped self-addressed envelope marked 'Prize Draw 94 Options' to the address below.

For a list of prize winners (available after 31st July 1994) send a stamped self-addressed envelope marked 'Prize Draw 94 Winners' to the address below.

Prize Draw address:
Mills & Boon Reader Service,
PO Box 236, Croydon, CR9 3RU.

Mills & Boon invite you to play
£600,000 LOTTO!

LOTTO CARD No: SA 789960

LOTTO SQUARES SCRATCH OFF

Instructions: Using a coin edge, scratch away 4 or 5 silver squares in a straight line (across, down or diagonally). If 5 hearts are revealed, this card is eligible to win the £600,000 Grand Prize: If 4 hearts, £25,000; 3 hearts, £6,000; 2 hearts, £3,000; 1 heart, £600. VOID IF MORE THAN 5 SILVER SQUARES ARE SCRATCHED AWAY.

AND...
YOU CAN CLAIM A MILLS & BOON ROMANCE ABSOLUTELY FREE AND WITH NO OBLIGATION

To register your entry in the draw and to claim your free book simply return this card. Don't forget to send us your address!

DON'T HESITATE - REPLY TODAY!

Over190 pages - worth at least £1.70 with the compliments of Mills & Boon

LOTTO REGISTRATION CARD

YES, please register my entry in the £600,000 Lotto Prize novel. I understand that I am under no obligation whatsoever. Draw. And, please send me my FREE Romantic

3A3PD

Ms / Mrs / Miss / Mr ——————————————————

Address ——————————————————

————————————— Postcode —————————————

Signature ——————————————————

Please note that the offer expires on 30th September 1993 and is subject to availability. Only one application per household. Readers overseas please send for postage details. In Southern Africa write to Book Services International Ltd., P.O. Box 24654, Craighall, transvaal 2024. You will receive further information from Mills & Boon about how you can receive more FREE books and gifts.

MILLS & BOON
READER SERVICE
FREEPOST
P.O. BOX 236
CROYDON
SURREY
CR9 9EL

NO
STAMP
NEEDED

Erin thought of resisting, but only for a moment. It was all so lovely—the warm, sweet-smelling air, the sheen over the water, even the croaking of an invisible frog somewhere quite near by. The stress of being in the same room as Jim and Priscilla had made her tense, but out here, alone with Brett, the tension was starting to vanish.

It was a minute or so before she became aware of things she had not noticed until then. Now she tried to ignore the corded thighs beneath her legs, the warm breath against her cheek, the hardness of the arm holding her shoulders.

'The perfume of the shrubs is intoxicating,' she said, over a primal hunger that was beginning to stir inside her.

'You are intoxicating,' Brett said softly. 'You inflame my senses, Erin, but I think you know that.'

'Don't, Brett.' She was scared suddenly. Whatever was coming, and no matter how much she wanted it in some part of her being, she was not ready for it yet.

'Come here,' he said, a hand cupping her neck as he drew her against him.

'No...'

She could not have said if the word made it past her lips in the moment before he began to kiss her; kisses that were so drugging that Erin, her senses already aroused, felt as if she was drowning in sensation. She began to make small moaning sounds as his tongue, teasing and tantalising the sensitive skin around her mouth, her throat, and then her mouth again, filled her with erotic pleasure. As his kisses became more and more passionate, demanding her response, insisting on it, she was filled with an aching hunger, and she opened her mouth to him.

Without loosening his hold on her lips, he began to caress her, his hands sliding over her throat, her ears, her arms, spreading fire wherever they touched. Against her body, his heartbeat was a wild, pounding thing, the fierceness of his desire filling Erin with exultation. Her limbs were weak with a need that was unlike anything she had ever known.

And then a hand was sliding beneath her dress to her breasts. At that moment, even while a part of her yearned for Brett to make love to her, sanity returned. Suddenly she understood quite how far she had let things go; that there would be no stopping if she did not call a halt quickly.

'No!' she gasped.

'All the time we were dancing I wanted to do this.' His voice was ragged with desire.

'Don't, Brett.' Pushing his hand from her breast, she pulled herself upright.

'Erin...?' A new note had come into his voice. 'Sweetheart, what's the matter?'

'This isn't what I want.'

'You wanted it a moment ago.'

'My defences were down,' she whispered unhappily.

His indrawn breath was an angry hiss. 'Are you nothing but a tease?' he demanded then.

'No...'

'You must have known this was going to happen when we came outside.'

'I didn't think about it,' she said on a sob. 'If I had, I wouldn't have come.'

'If you didn't want me to kiss you, Erin, then what the hell was happening on the dance-floor?' he demanded.

'Brett...' she began, and stopped.

'I didn't imagine the way you cuddled against me. You were the initiator, Erin, I took my cue from you.'

'I know that,' she admitted unhappily.

'Well, then?'

'Jim and Priscilla...' Once more she stopped.

The long body tensed. Beneath her legs Erin felt the bunching of hard muscles. She sensed Brett's fury even before he spoke.

'So that's what it was all about.'

'I thought you knew,' she whispered.

'You were trying to make Jim jealous,' he grated.

'Not exactly. Brett, you're so angry...'

'Damn right I am! How dare you play me for a fool, Erin?'

'I wasn't trying to do that,' she faltered.

'Are you still in love with Jim?'

'I don't know... I'm not sure... But we were to have been married today. Tonight would have been our wedding night. Tomorrow would have been the start of our lives together. I've thought of nothing else all year, Brett. It was traumatic walking in on the two of them the other day, but watching them on the dance-floor was painful too.' She paused, then said, 'I thought you'd understand.'

'I understand that you feel humiliated by Jim's behaviour—that's only natural. As for the rest—how do you explain the fact that you were responding to me a few minutes ago?'

'I got carried away,' she said miserably.

'Were you pretending I was Jim? That Jim was kissing you?'

Not for a moment had Brett been Jim in Erin's mind. She could not remember, even once, responding to Jim as she had responded to Brett.

'Well, Erin?' His voice was a whiplash.

'I wish you weren't quite so angry,' she said unsteadily.

'I'm not your toy, Erin. Jim treated you abominably, but I will not be used by you to make him or anyone else jealous, the sooner you understand that the better.'

'Brett, please——'

The words she had been about to say died on her lips as he put her away from him. She had to find her feet quickly as, without warning, he stood up.

'If you want me to take you back to the dance, I'll walk you as far as the main building,' he said curtly.

'I couldn't go back there. I just want to go to my room.'

'Fine.'

Silently—a painful silence now—they made their way along the path that led to the rondavels. Erin put her key in the lock and opened the door. When she turned to say goodnight, Brett had already vanished in the darkness.

CHAPTER SIX

ERIN was awake at dawn the next morning. Her head throbbed and her eyes burned with fatigue and with the tears she had shed after Brett had left her so abruptly. The light that came through her windows was grey and a little bleak, and when she pushed aside the blanket and looked outside she saw that it was drizzling. She was tempted to crawl back into bed, to burrow beneath the sheet where nobody would see her.

But there was something she had to do, and the sooner she did it the better.

When she had showered and washed her hair, she felt a little better. Pulling on jeans, a sweater and a nylon jacket which had seen duty in many a spring snowfall, she left the rondavel.

Brett was nowhere to be seen. He was not in the main building, or in the gardens. Approaching his rondavel, Erin saw that the place had an empty look. She knocked on the door, but was not surprised when there was no response.

She had left the stables for last. Brett was not there either, nor was the horse he usually rode. The stable-hands were not on duty yet, but after years of farming life Erin knew how to handle a horse. The mare she had ridden on her first morning at Hilltop Inn was a gentle steed who knew her now, and she stood quite still as Erin saddled her.

The countryside looked different beneath the heavy sky—brooding and mysterious. The birds that usually called from the trees were still, and in the forest that air smelled even danker than usual.

When Erin had left the hotel grounds, she kept her eyes on the trail, searching for signs that Brett had come this way. There were many hoofmarks, but mostly they looked old. And then, on some freshly fallen pine-needles, she saw prints that could only have been made recently, and she knew she was headed in the right direction.

Because she was looking out for him, she saw him before he noticed her. He was proceeding down a slope, a lithe figure sitting easily astride a stallion that seemed to have strength in common with its rider. Watching him, so overwhelmingly masculine, Erin felt the same stirring which she had experienced the previous night at the pool, and she wished with all her heart that Jim had not de-stroyed her trust in men.

Brett's head lifted suddenly, so that she knew he had seen her. Momentarily he slowed his horse, then he came to meet her.

'Hello, prairie girl,' he said as he reined in the stallion. 'What are you doing in the forests at this hour and in this weather? Or do you enjoy communing with nature in the rain?'

'I came out to find you,' she told him.

Brett regarded her steadily a few seconds. His lips were tilted fractionally at the corners, but his jaw had a strong, unyielding look. 'Why, Erin?'

'So that I could apologise for last night.'

'Ah.' There was a gleam in his eyes now.

'You were right to be angry with me, because it was true—in a sense I was using you to get back at Jim. I shouldn't have done that.'

'In a sense, Erin? Are you saying that wasn't the only reason?'

Erin's voice was low. 'Jim and Priscilla's togetherness made me feel very lonely. Perhaps you'd think it wouldn't have bothered me, that I should have accepted the situation by now—and in a way, Brett, I have—but it's the way it was last night.'

The two horses were so close together on the trail now that Brett was able to reach out his hand and touch her face. She sat quite still as he traced a path from her lips up to her eyes, then pushed a few damp strands of hair from her forehead.

'You're wet,' he said, as he threaded his fingers through her hair.

'So are you, Brett.'

'I'm used to it.'

She laughed. 'I am too.'

'Nevertheless ... Did you ride out in the rain just to apologise?'

'Yes.'

'Want to ride a little further with me before you go back to the hotel and get into some dry clothes?' he asked.

'Does that mean you haven't decided to fire me?'

'I've never had any intention of doing that,' he said softly. 'Imagine all the fine chocolates that would have been wasted.' He was teasing, but his voice had the sound of a caress.

'Imagine,' Erin said, over a tide of inexplicable happiness.

As they rode through the forests, with the rain falling softly through the tree-tops, Erin did not care that her hair and her clothes were wet. Side by side on the trail, they talked about many things, but, as if by agreement, they did not mention Jim.

They were almost back at the stables when Brett turned to her. 'We'll set out tomorrow in search of products for your store,' he told her.

They left Hilltop Inn immediately after breakfast the next morning. Erin had packed a small suitcase, for Brett had said they would probably spend at least one night away from the hotel.

As they left the forests behind them, they came to farming country—citrus and avocados and some tobacco and tea. Now and then they travelled through areas that were uncultivated—*bushveld*, Brett called it.

'A little like the prairies in some ways,' Erin said, 'yet quite different too.'

She stared out of the window, enchanted with the tropical countryside. There were umbrella-shaped trees called acacias, and other trees called maroelas. Here and there were stretches where shrubs had been planted by the side of the road—scarlet and purple bougainvillaea, pink and white oleanders and flame-coloured hibiscus. Most amazing of all, in Erin's eyes, were the wild palms with bananas and papayas hanging from their branches.

Brett had phoned ahead, and so wherever they went they were expected and welcomed. Farming wives were happy to show off their produce. Some things Erin had expected—canned fruit, honey made from local bees, pickled tomatoes and onions and cucumbers. But there were other wares too, some of them unfamiliar. Erin had never eaten *konfyt*, a sweet-tasting preserve made of watermelon, or dried figs, or the sticky confection called *koeksusters*. With delight, she chewed a spicy stick of *biltong*, dried meat which resembled beef jerky, yet was not quite the same. She admired embroidered tray-cloths and crocheted tea-cosies and knitted baby layettes. She particularly loved the batiks made by a woman who was both a farmer and an artist, and listened with rapt attention to the details of how they were made—the cloth illustrated and waxed, and undergoing many immersions in different dyes.

'Well?' Brett asked, when they were driving away from the batik artist.

'I love it! All of it.'

'Think you can make a go of the store?'

'I'm sure of it. I'd no idea we'd find such a wealth of talent, Brett.'

'I'm less surprised than you are,' he told her. 'I always knew there was talent here, ready to be tapped.' Turning his eyes from the road, he grinned at her. 'The *pièce de résistance*, of course, will be your chocolates.'

'I was thinking, if there's demand for them, I could make speciality cakes as well. I've made many birthday cakes. A few wedding cakes too...' Her lips trembled.

'Great!' Brett said briskly.

There was silence a few moments. Then Erin said, 'You'll have to find someone else to run the shop for you when I leave.'

The dark eyes turned once more from the road. 'Do you think so?'

Such an odd response, she thought, but decided not to take him up on it. She found she did not want to know who would take over the store when she was gone.

She was disturbingly aware of Brett now. He was wearing shorts, and his tanned thighs were taut on the seat beside her, reminding her of their hardness when she'd sat on his lap by the moonlit pool. Without warning, she was hit by a fierce stab of desire, and she turned her head quickly away from Brett and to the window. If she had wanted to, she could not have spoken.

In the late afternoon they found themselves in a village that was so tiny that Erin wondered if an unsuspecting tourist would have spotted it. 'Village' was almost too grand a description for the collection of houses huddled together in the midst of farming land. It was more of a hamlet, really, situated on a dirt-road, far away from any highway.

Brett drew up in front of an inn. 'This is as far as we're going today,' he said.

'We're going to be spending the night *here*?'

'Right.'

'Two rooms,' Erin said, a little too quickly.

His grin was wicked. 'Sure of that, Erin?'

'Quite,' she said, over a rapidly beating heart.

'Pity.' His grin was more wicked still.

The inn was tiny; no more than a handful of people stayed there at any one time, Brett said. The clerk at the desk treated them to a cynical glance, before assigning them to adjoining rooms.

'You can lock the door if that will make you feel safer,' Brett told her, when he had carried their bags to their rooms.

Erin threw him a spirited look. 'I always do that now anyway.'

'Sensible. Feel like exploring the surroundings before dark, Erin?'

'Love to.'

The village was so small that a few minutes after Erin and Brett had walked out of the inn they had left the last of the houses behind them. They turned off the road and on to a trail that took them through open *veld* with long, wild grass as far as the eye could see. In the distance was a line of willows.

A hush lay over the land. The sun was setting, and the sky was awash with colours more vivid than any Erin had ever seen before coming to Africa—crimson and orange and long streaks of bright gold.

'A primitive kind of sunset,' she said. 'I'd no idea this continent was so beautiful, Brett.'

His hand brushed against hers. 'Stay here long enough, and you may not want to leave it.'

'I have to go back,' she said, over a heaviness in her chest and throat. 'You know that, Brett.'

'Do I?'

'Just as soon as I've saved enough to pay for my flights.'

He did not answer. As he looked down at her, the setting sun lit his face and was reflected in his eyes, making it impossible to read their expression. A kind of pain gnawed in Erin's loins, and restlessly she widened the gap between Brett and herself.

Reaching the willows, they found themselves at a stream. The shore of the stream was rocky, and Brett reached for Erin's hand as they clambered from one rock to another. For once she made no move to resist him, and after a few seconds his fingers interlaced with hers. Involuntarily, her eyes wandered to the two clasped hands, the larger one folded over the smaller one. Her breath made a skittering sound in her throat and, looking up, she saw that Brett was watching her.

They found a rock and leaned back against it. Erin's eyes were on the stream now—at least that was safe to look at. A bird made a loud, clattering sound in the branches of a tree, another bird responded. Then all was still once more.

It was almost dark when they stood up and made their way back along the trail. In the inn, lights were shining in the windows now, and a few of the houses had smoke rising from their chimneys.

In the small dining-room, Erin and Brett ate together. The menu was short, but the simple food was delicious. Long after they had finished eating, they still sat talking. As she watched Brett's amused expression when he made a forceful point, it occurred to Erin that she could not recall one in-depth conversation with Jim. After just a few days, she knew more about Brett than she had learned about her fiancé, even after a year of letters.

When Brett had paid the bill, she glanced at her watch. 'I'd no idea it was so late!' she exclaimed. 'It doesn't seem possible that we could have been sitting here for more than three hours.'

'Time passes quickly when two people get on well together.' Brett's expression was enigmatic.

Erin left the comment unanswered.

At the door of her room, she turned. 'Goodnight, Brett.'

'It could be a better one, Erin.' His tone was seductively husky.

She stood very still as he cupped her chin in his hand, and brushed a long finger sensuously down her throat. Her body was treacherously yielding as he drew her against him. His kiss was tender, undemanding, filled with a sweetness that made her ache with a longing that was becoming too familiar.

It did not take her long to brush her teeth and change into a nightgown. Wryly she looked at herself in the mirror. The nightgown had been a gift from the friends she had worked with. Pale pink, with delicate lace at the neck and hem, it was almost transparent—just the thing, her friends had teased, for a bride on her honeymoon.

She switched off the light beside the door and got into bed, but after a few minutes she knew she was too wound up to sleep. There was a lamp beside her bed. She switched it on with a snap of her fingers, then got out of bed to look for the paperback she'd packed in her suitcase.

She was about to reach for the book when she saw it. Bigger than an insect, it had eight legs and a curved tail—vicious-looking, dangerous.

Erin jumped backwards with a scream. Seconds later she was pounding on the door of Brett's room.

In an instant he had opened the door. 'Why, Erin...'

'Something awful in my room, Brett!' she gasped.

His eyes swept the white face. 'What?' he asked then.

'I'm not sure. It's on the floor by my bed.'

'Wait here.'

'Brett...' And when he looked back at her, 'Be careful.'

When he had left the room she sat down on his bed, bare feet curled beneath her. On the other side of the wall she heard two loud thumps. There was the sound of the inn door opening and then closing.

Two minutes after Brett had left her, he was back.

'What was it?' she asked.

'A scorpion.'

'A *scorpion*?' She stared at him in horror.

'Nobody's favourite pet. I take it you've never seen one before?'

'No, though I've heard of them. It looked vicious.'

'It's not nice, but it's gone now, Erin,' he assured her.

'Could there be any more?' she asked anxiously.

Brett hesitated a moment. 'Probably not.'

'A mate, Brett?'

'It's unlikely.'

Erin tried to suppress a shudder as she uncurled herself from the bed and stood up. 'Thanks,' she said through trembling lips.

'You don't have to go back there, Erin,' he said quietly. 'You can stay here with me.'

She was tempted, so tempted. And not only because of the scorpion.

Her voice was unsteady. 'I don't know...'

He came towards her. She was trembling again, but for a different reason this time. She saw his eyes taking in her body beneath the transparency of the nightgown.

'I knew you'd be lovely,' he said huskily.

She took a step backwards, warding off danger of a new sort now—a far greater danger than a scorpion, which could be disposed of with two thumps.

'I think I'd better go.' Her voice shook.

'You don't really want to return to that room, Erin.'

'The scorpion is gone,' she reminded him.

'I want you to stay.' The look in the eyes that never left her body was unnerving.

'Brett——'

'I believe you want to stay too, Erin.'

She stared at him, unable to get out the one word she knew she should say. And then it was too late, for he had closed the gap between them and was drawing her into his arms. They stood together for a time without meaning, her legs tilted forward, her neck arched back, her thighs pressed hard against his legs.

As he began to kiss her, slowly, sensuously, she was kissing him back with an abandon she had not known she possessed. His hands slid over her waist, then her hips, pulling her even closer against him. Desire gripped her, deep and savage, and she was holding him too now, both of them straining, wanting, needing to be as close as possible.

She did not resist when he lifted her into his arms and put her down on the bed—for the moment she was past thought, past resistance. Brett lay down beside her, and it was better that way, because their lips were on the same level now. They were touching again, hands learning the shape and feel of each other's bodies. As Brett caressed Erin's soft skin, her fingers fastened convulsively on hard bone and muscle. She shuddered as his lips left her mouth and his tongue began to draw long, erotic strokes over her throat. She gasped as his hands reached beneath the low cut of her nightgown and went to her breasts, and her nipples hardened in seconds beneath his fingers. She did not resist when he drew the nightgown up and over her shoulders. She was not ashamed of her nakedness, because she was barely aware of it.

'You're so beautiful, Erin.' His voice was ragged.

He bent his head, and she was unable to move as he began to kiss her where no man's lips had ever been. He caught her nipples between his lips, first the one nipple, then the other, ignoring her soft whimpering as he kissed her.

After a while he raised himself on one elbow. 'Undress me too, Erin.'

Eyes dazed with shock and need and longing, she stared up at him. For the first time, she realised quite how far she had allowed things to proceed.

'Brett...' she began through swollen lips.

'Hurry, darling. Erin, sweetheart, don't you know what to do?'

'There's something you need to know...'

'We'll talk later,' he said huskily.

'Brett—I'm a virgin,' she whispered.

The words made an impact. '*What*?'

'You're shocked.'

The hands on her body had stilled. 'You and Jim never made love?'

'I wanted to wait until our wedding,' she explained.

Brett's body was tight and hard. 'Why are you telling me this now?'

'Because I'm frightened.'

'I'd never hurt you, Erin, don't you know that?'

Her body ached with unfulfilled longing. There was a part of her that yearned for the release which only Brett could give her. It was her mind which made her draw back. 'It's still so soon after...'

Brett looked very angry all at once. 'I don't believe you're saying this,' he hissed. 'Next you'll be telling me again that if you let me make love to you it would only be because you're still on the rebound from Jim.'

'Yes...' She recoiled before the look in his face, yet she knew she had to be honest with him.

'How can you even *think* such a thing? Especially now, when we're both so aroused?'

'I didn't mean this to happen.' Her throat was thick with tears.

'I didn't force you to do a damn thing you didn't want to do yourself,' he said furiously. 'You've wanted this as much as I have. Admit it, Erin!'

'I do admit it,' she said unhappily.

'Then what is it? What's gone wrong?'

'My feelings about men haven't changed,' she told him.

'That's over! What just happened between us proved that.'

'No. It's only three days since Jim and I...since we were to have been married.'

'Are you *still* using me as a substitute for him? Is that what this is all about? Did you come to my room wearing that damned seductive garment because you were so frustrated at not having sex with the bum that you wanted me to make love to you instead?'

'I came because I saw the scorpion.'

'And enjoyed every moment that followed—until you thought of your rotten fiancé.'

'Yes...' she muttered.

'When will you realise that Jim is in the past? Dammit, Erin, you wanted me—still do, if you're truthful. You're just as attracted to me as I am to you. Do you really believe that what you did with me you'd have done with any man?'

She choked back tears. 'I can't be certain.'

'Don't put yourself down like this. Don't do it to yourself, Erin. Can't you trust your own feelings?'

'Not yet.'

'When?'

'Maybe never.'

'*Why*?' he demanded.

'I'm so frightened of being hurt again,' she said, her voice low with despair.

Brett stood up, his expression hard. 'Get beneath the sheets, Erin.'

'Where are you going?' she whispered.

'I'll sleep in your room tonight. You can stay here in mine.'

'There could be another scorpion,' she warned.

'I'll chance it. What I will not do, in any circumstances, is spend the night in the same bed as you. Not even in the same room. I'm a normal man, Erin. If I slept here tonight, I'd try to make love to you again. And if I did that, I might not be able to respect myself. Nor would I be able to stop.'

'I could sleep on the chair,' she said.

He grinned at that. 'I haven't stooped to accepting that kind of chivalry from a woman.'

He was at the door when she said, 'Brett...I'm so sorry.'

'I'm sorry too. Just one bit of advice before I leave, Erin—don't ever use me as a substitute for Jim again.'

CHAPTER SEVEN

ERIN rose early the morning after the trip to begin work in the cottage which Brett had said she could use for the store. The cottage was in an ideal position, between the main building and the rondavels, where guests could not help but see it.

Erin's Place. Hilltop Inn Gifts had been Erin's suggestion, but the name they had settled on had been Brett's final choice.

The moment she unlocked the door, she saw that changes had taken place in her absence. The interior of the cottage had been painted, as well as the outside. Attractive wooden shelves lined two of the walls, and a long, rustic-looking table, evidently meant to serve duty as a counter, stood near the third wall.

Liz, on her way to Reception, stopped in the open doorway. 'Erin's Place. Doesn't it look terrific?'

'Amazing! I can't believe so much was done in such a short time. Brett and I were only away two days.'

Liz laughed. 'When you know Brett Mallory a little better, you'll understand that he's a man who gets things done. When he wants something, he usually goes after it with determination.'

Erin's head swung up. 'Is he always successful?' she asked.

'Most of the time. Say, Erin, I really like what's been done with this place. There's just enough here for you to get to work, little enough so that you can impose your own ideas on the store.'

'And I do have ideas, lots of them,' Erin said eagerly. Remembering the coolness that had spoiled the latter part of her trip with Brett, she added in a quieter tone, 'If I'm here long enough to implement them, that is.'

'Still planning to return to Canada at the first opportunity?' Liz asked.

'More than ever.'

'Brett won't like it,' Liz warned.

'What do you mean by that?' A strange pain in Erin's chest made her voice unsteady.

'Surely you don't need it spelled out for you? You must know that he's interested in you.'

'If that was true at some point, I doubt it is now,' sighed Erin.

'Something happen while you were away?' Liz's eyes were warmly compassionate rather than curious.

Erin hesitated. She had taken to the freckle-faced receptionist the first time they'd met, and in the space of a few days they had become friends. She knew she could confide in Liz if she needed someone to talk to, but she found that her feelings for Brett, and what had happened between them, were personal in a way that seemed to defy discussion.

'Mind if I don't talk about it, Liz?' she said.

'Of course, not.' Liz hesitated, then said, 'May I say one thing, though?'

'You can tell me anything—you know that.'

'Jim Saunders is not the man Brett is.'

'That's what Brett keeps telling me too, and I do know it's true,' Erin said slowly. 'I also know that I'm not ready for another relationship with a man. I may never be. Besides, Liz, however much I like it here, this isn't my home.'

'It could be.'

Erin shook her head. 'I don't think so. Which is not to say that I won't make the most of my time while I'm here.'

She spent the rest of the day doing just that. By lunchtime, the wares which Erin and Brett had brought back with them the previous day had been set out attractively. Jars of pickled onions, mushrooms and cucumbers filled two shelves. Three other shelves were taken up with a colourful display of honeys and jams and marmalades. Embroidered tray-cloths hung over the back of a chair which Erin had purloined from the stock-room, and a heap of crocheted tea-cosies had been arranged with deceptive casualness on a low stool. The batiks were tacked carefully to the empty wall. On the table stood a lovely ceramic vase which Erin filled with dahlias and roses from the garden.

Next morning she was visited by a representative from a flooring company. He arrived with samples of carpeting, vinyl and ceramic tiles. Tiles would be perfect for the look of the store, Erin decided, and she asked the salesman if he would leave a few samples with her, so that she could consider them at her leisure.

Later that day she took a walk through the garden. In a wooded area, where few guests seemed to go, she found precisely what she needed—a piece of irregular-shaped wood. When she had sanded and oiled the wood, she carefully burned into it the words 'Erin's Place'. Taking care that the nails did not extend all the way through the wood, she hammered the sign on to the exterior wall of the cottage, beside the door. If Brett decided to rename the gift store after her departure from Hilltop Inn, he would be able to remove the sign and replace it with another.

Erin left her chocolates for last. With the store ready for customers, she took a ride into town with Liz on the receptionist's day off. They did not go to Nelspruit, where Erin had left the train, but to Sabie, a town that was much closer to the forests. In Sabie she stocked up on ingredients.

In the hotel kitchen, under the reluctant eye of the main chef, she began to make a few of her choicest confections: rum balls and truffles and tiny squares filled with nuts; chocolates shaped like swans and mice and rabbits. Hot work, tiring—yet immensely rewarding as well. When Erin stood back a few days later and surveyed two shelves of chocolates, some arranged in trays, others wrapped in Cellophane and topped with tiny silk bows, she felt a sense of immense achievement.

Early the next morning she went to the stables, where she knew that she would find Brett. In the days since their trip they had spent almost no time together; when they did see each other, their conversation was confined to talk of the store. It was as if the night of the scorpion was still so vivid in both their minds that they could not talk of more mundane things.

She stopped at the entrance to the stables. Brett, just returned from his ride, was lifting the saddle from his horse. As she watched him, her eyes taking in the strong arms and throat, the play of muscles beneath his shirt, the thick dark hair curling at the top of his neck, memory of the night at the inn flooded her unbidden. Desire gripped her, hot and fierce, flushing her cheeks and making her legs weak. Momentarily she closed her eyes, as if by so doing she could shut out the sensations flooding her body.

'Good morning, Erin.'

She forced herself to open her eyes and look at him. 'Hi, Brett.'

'If I'd known you wanted to ride with me, I'd have waited for you,' he told her.

'That's not why I'm here.'

'Really?'

Just one word, but spoken so mockingly that it seemed as if he knew precisely the effect he was having on her—and derived satisfaction from the knowledge.

'I came to tell you that I'm ready for business,' she added.

'Ah,' he said blandly.

She was suddenly very angry. Lifting her head at him, she said, 'I've put enormous effort into fixing up the store, but you don't really care about it one way or the other, do you, Brett?'

Without warning, he stepped away from the horse and gripped her shoulders. 'But I do care,' he said, very softly. 'I thought you knew that.'

He was so close to her that her nostrils were filled with a composite smell of sweat and horse and aftershave, a combination that was so intoxicating that it made her feel dizzy.

'You do know it, Erin, don't you?'

She stared up at him, mesmerised by the expression in his eyes, caught by the odd intensity in his voice. Her breathing quickened as she was rocked by an even greater wave of desire. It would take very little persuasion on Brett's part for her to go into his arms right here, in the stables. If he coaxed her to the ground, and tried to make love to her on the hay, she might not be able to resist him. And wouldn't that be a difficult memory to forget when she had left Hilltop Inn!

Abruptly she moved out of his hands and took a few steps away from him.

'Perhaps you do care,' she said coolly. 'I guess there'd have been no point in going to the expense of paint and shelves and flooring if you didn't.'

His eyes gleamed. 'You tell me, Erin.'

'I just did,' she said shortly.

'Of course,' he replied, careless insolence in his voice.

'Anyway,' she said, making an effort to control her breathing, 'I thought you'd want to know that I'm going to open today.'

'Looking forward to it, Erin?' he asked.

'I hope I'll do well.'

'I know you'll do very well indeed.'

He reached out a hand and traced a finger around her face: around her lips, her eyes, lazily past her mouth to her throat.

'*Don't*!' she said.

'I'm sorry.' But his voice sounded anything but apologetic as his hand dropped to his side. 'Why do I keep forgetting that you don't like to be touched? Do you suppose it's because your words say one thing while your body language seems to suggest something quite different?'

She treated him to a furious look, then turned on her heel. As she strode out of the stables, she heard his low laugh. The sound did nothing to improve her mood.

Erin's Place was a success from the day it opened. The hotel guests, walking past the little cottage on the way from their rondavels to the main building, would wander in and spend a while looking around. Although they did not always come in with the purpose of buying, mostly they did make a few purchases before their stay at Hilltop

Inn ended. The local jams and honeys were favourites from the start, and the batiks elicited much enthusiasm. But it was Erin's chocolates which were in more demand than anything else. So quickly were they snapped up that she was constantly having to replenish her stock.

When word got out that she was an expert baker, she was commissioned to make a cake for a young man's twenty-first birthday party. So professional was that cake that orders began to come in for other cakes. People, it seemed, were prepared to pay for well-made speciality confections.

'At the rate you're selling your things, it won't be long before you have enough saved up to pay for your journey home,' Liz remarked when she arrived to tell Erin about yet another order.

'It's certainly going more quickly than I ever dreamed it would,' Erin agreed.

'Will you be sorry to leave?' Liz asked curiously.

'I want very much to go home, but it will be hard to say goodbye to...to people.'

Actually, Erin was beginning to suspect that the farewells would be heart-wrenching. A fact that she would be careful to keep to herself when the time came.

Sunday. The one day when Erin's Place was closed. Lying in bed, listening to the birds and watching the swaying of trees through the open window, Erin stretched luxuriously beneath the sheets. It was bliss to sleep in one day a week, for she was putting in long hours at the store now. She wondered what she could do that day. Momentarily her thoughts went to Brett—a ride through the forests would be heavenly—but she pushed the picture of a rugged face firmly from her mind. Since the day the store had opened, she had seen little of him. Her own fault, perhaps, for she had taken to avoiding him.

It was a day to be out of doors, she decided. She would spend the morning at the pool with a book and a bottle of sun-tan oil. In the afternoon she would look for a tennis partner.

Plans made, she got out of bed. When she was dressed in turquoise shorts and a matching halter-necked blouse, she left the rondavel and walked along the path to the main building. Brett would not be about at this hour, but a few of the hotel guests stopped and spoke to her, and at the desk Gloria, Liz's weekend replacement, called out a friendly good morning as well.

Erin smiled at the waiter as he took her breakfast order. It was going to be a good day.

'Hello, Erin.'

The smile left her face as she looked up at Brett, and her treacherous heart began to beat a little faster. He was grinning down at her, eyes dark and sparkling.

'I was looking for you, prairie girl,' he said.

She forced herself to look at him calmly. 'Oh?'

'Made any plans for today?'

'Swimming, sunning and tennis,' she told him.

'How would you like to do the first two at Wayne Anderson's farm? You remember him, don't you, the widower with the two children?'

The smile reappeared in Erin's eyes. 'And a puppy aptly named Scraggles.'

'Right. The Andersons would like you to spend the day with them.'

She hesitated a moment. 'Are you coming too, Brett?'

'Would it bother you if I said yes?' he asked.

'I just wondered.'

'Wayne invited us both. But here's a thought to add to your wondering, Erin—in the company of Wayne and his children, I'm hardly likely to annoy you with any amorous attention.'

'I can take care of myself,' she said lightly.

'You can, can't you?' he drawled. 'Shall I tell Wayne it's yes, then?'

'I'd like that,' Erin said. They left the hotel half an hour later. Besides her swimsuit and towel, Erin took along two packets of chocolate. Brett switched on the radio—they seemed to enjoy the same music—and Erin put down her window and let the wind blow through her hair. Now and then she turned her head and glanced at the strong shape of Brett's profile. Once he turned his head and caught her eyes, but he did not speak. He just smiled, and after a moment she found herself smiling back.

Tim and Amy must have been watching for them, for as the car drew to a halt in front of the farmhouse the children ran into the yard. Their father followed seconds later. Erin and Brett were getting out of the car when Scraggles appeared as well, barking and jumping with excitement.

'My, but he's grown!' Erin exclaimed, picking up the puppy and holding him against her. 'I can't believe this is the frightened little dog I held on my lap just a short time ago.'

Wayne laughed. 'You can almost watch them grow at this stage of their lives. And this one's growing quicker than most.'

'But it's not even three weeks since I saw him.'

'That much?' Wayne made a rueful face. 'I feel very guilty. The children have been at me to invite Brett and the nice lady who rescued their puppy, but I've been so busy cleaning up after the storm that I've had no time to entertain.'

'Erin has been busy too,' Brett told him.

'I heard something about a store,' Wayne said. 'You must tell me all about it.'

The smile left Erin's face. 'If you know about the store, Wayne, then you must also know that my wedding never took place.'

'Yes,' he said quietly. 'I'm sorry.'

'Obviously you weren't surprised.'

'Unfortunately not,' he agreed.

The memory of that first humiliating day brought a painful thickness to Erin's throat. She would *not* let herself cry! Not here, not today.

Bending her head, she opened her bag. By the time she had taken out the gifts she'd brought with her, she had managed to swallow back her tears.

Straightening once more, she found Brett watching her. About to send him a silent message telling him that she was in no mood for his sarcasm, she saw admiration in his eyes instead.

Suddenly it was easy to smile at Wayne and the children.

'Look what I brought you,' she said.

Faces rapt and excited, the children opened their gifts. Amy's chocolate was in the shape of a mouse, Tim's looked like a rabbit.

'I think Miss Leroy made these herself,' said their father.

'Let them call me Erin,' she said. 'And yes, I did make the chocolates.'

'Wow!' exclaimed the children with one breath.

Erin smiled at them. 'Unless you plan to eat the chocolates right away, maybe you'd like to put them somewhere cool, so they won't melt?'

'Why don't we all get some shade?' Wayne suggested. 'Erin . . . Brett . . . I hope you brought your swimsuits? Great! Let's go and sit under the umbrella by the pool, then I want to hear all about Erin's Place.'

'What are you thinking, Erin?'

'How did you know I was thinking about anything in particular, Brett?'

'That blissful look as you gaze over the pool.'

Erin laughed. 'If you must know, I was looking at the sparkling water, at the bright sky and those citrus trees all around us, and I was wondering if I'd strayed into a little piece of paradise. And then I pictured my parents' home as it would look like right now—fields under a few feet of snow, Dad ploughing the snow on the driveway, Mom scraping the frost from her windscreen before she can leave for work every day. Both of them leaving home a little earlier than they would in summer, because their cars might skid on the icy roads if they drive too fast.'

'Quite a picture,' Wayne said.

'Makes you wonder why she doesn't decide to stay here permanently, doesn't it?' Brett remarked.

Erin sat up. 'I can't stay here because this isn't my home,' she explained.

'It nearly was.'

'Things changed—as you well know.'

Without looking at Brett, Erin stood up. 'I'm going to swim,' she said, and walked to the water.

At the edge of the pool, she glanced at the two men. They were both watching her, neither of them making any attempt to disguise their interest in her figure. She raised her arms, took a breath, and dived into the water— a neat dive that caused barely a splash. The water was warm and lovely, and she swam a few lengths without stopping.

She was unaware of the picture she made as she left the water and walked back to the umbrella in the lilac bikini she had bought for her honeymoon—long, lovely limbs; tiny waist; swell of round breasts at the top of the bikini; green eyes sparkling beneath long wet lashes; golden hair, darker now that it was wet, clinging to her head. What she did see was the intent expressions on the faces of the two men. Feeling suddenly self-conscious, she took a comb from her bag, ran it through her wet hair, then put on her sunglasses and lay back in a long chair.

A welcome diversion appeared in the form of the children. They arrived at the pool, Tim with Scraggles in his arms, Amy with a book.

'Hey,' Erin said, 'would you like me to read to you?'

They settled themselves on either side of her. When Erin had read the children a few stories, she began to tell them about her home. Their eyes, so much like their father's, grew wide as she told them about snow and skating and skiing. They wanted to hear about her childhood, about the things she and her brothers had got up to when they were young.

Lunch was a *braaivleis*: barbecued steak and chops and buttered *mielies*, and sticky *koeksusters* for dessert. Tim and Amy sat down beside Erin with their plates. Later they insisted she join them in the pool for a boisterous game they called 'water-ball'.

When they emerged from the water at last, both children were shivering, and their father told them to go indoors and change into dry clothes.

Erin was smiling as she watched them walk towards the house. 'You're lucky, Wayne, they're both darlings,' she told him.

'They are. I apologise for the way they've monopolised you all day.'

'I enjoyed myself as much as they did,' she assured him.

'They miss their mother,' Wayne said, and Erin saw that his eyes were sad.

The sun was beginning to set, and Brett said it was time to be going. When Erin went into the house to change her clothes, she saw that the hours by the water had brought an extra tan to her face and freckles to her nose. The children walked with her to the car.

'Will you come again, Erin?' Tim asked.

'I'd like that.'

Amy tugged on her hand. 'Will you marry our daddy?'

There were a few seconds of shocked silence. Erin saw that Wayne looked embarrassed. Brett's face was without expression.

'*Amy!*' Wayne said then.

'It's OK.' Erin smiled at the little girl. 'What I would like is to visit you again some time, Amy.'

'We'd all like that,' said Wayne.

Erin waved through the window to the children and their father. It had been such a good day that she was still smiling as Brett turned the car and drove down the farm road. With darkness approaching, a calmness had settled over the citrus orchards. Once a few monkeys scampered over the road, then all was still once more.

Erin did not know when she realised that Brett was unusually quiet. Glancing sideways, she noticed a tightness around his mouth.

'Didn't you enjoy the day?' she asked.

'More to the point, Erin, did you?'

'Very much. But I get the feeling something's bothering you. What is it, Brett?'

'The thought,' he said, his voice sounding so strange, 'that I might have been all kinds of a fool to accept Wayne Anderson's invitation.'

A week passed. Saturday evening came and went, and Jim did not bring his girlfriend to the dance. Nor did he come to the hotel during the week, for a beer in the bar, or to play darts with some of the other locals for whom Hilltop Inn was a social meeting-place. Erin was beginning to wonder if her erstwhile fiancé intended to keep away from the hotel permanently. It would make her stay here much easier if that were to be the case.

Another week went by. Another Saturday. It was late afternoon, and there was a lift in Erin's step as she left the store and walked along the shrub-lined path to her rondavel. Life at Hilltop Inn was turning out to be far more pleasant than she had dreamed it could be. She tried not to think about her relationship with Brett, but Erin's Place was becoming more successful all the time, giving her a constant sense of pleasure and achievement. Sales of her chocolates were brisk, and her bank account was swelling by the day.

Jasmine covered the walls of her rondavel, filling her bedroom with a lovely fragrance, especially at night. Outside the door, she stopped to pick a few sprigs, then walked inside. As she put the sweet-smelling flowers in a glass of water, she smiled to herself at the thought of the evening that lay ahead. She loved music and dancing, and a social evening was a nice way to end the week.

She decided to wear another of the dresses she had acquired for her honeymoon—a dress that was a blending of blue and green and turquoise, mini-skirted, with soft pleats flowing naturally from a dropped waist. On impulse, she stuck a piece of jasmine in her hair.

She turned from the mirror as a knock sounded on her door. Brett stood outside the rondavel. Brett, in white trousers and an open-necked navy shirt, tall and lean and rugged, and more attractive than any man Erin knew.

For a long moment he stood quite still. Erin's heart skittered against her ribs as she saw his eyes take in every detail of her appearance.

'I thought I'd see if you were ready for the dance,' he said. Voice turning husky, he added, 'You look very beautiful, Erin.'

Brett steered her towards a table at the edge of the dance-floor. Some people were sitting at tables, others were already moving to the disc jockey's lively music.

Filled with the tremulousness that had been with her since Brett's unexpected arrival at her rondavel, Erin did not register faces. It was only when Brett broke off abruptly in the middle of a sentence that she knew something was amiss. Following the direction of his eyes, she turned her head and saw Jim walk into the room with his mistress.

'Stay cool,' Brett advised quietly, as Jim looked their way.

Jim muttered something to Priscilla, then he walked over to the table where Erin and Brett were sitting.

Ignoring Brett, he said, 'So you're still here, Erin.'

'I told you I would be,' she reminded him.

'It's a big country, I asked you to find a job elsewhere.'

Beneath the table, Brett put a hand on Erin's leg. The touch was not lascivious; rather, it was intended to give her courage, so that she was able to say, 'What I do is my own choice. It has nothing to do with you.'

'You're determined to stay, then?'

'For the moment,' she said, wondering how she could have fallen in love with this man.

Jim turned to Brett. 'I suppose it was your idea to set up my fiancée in a gift store?'

'Ex-fiancée, I believe,' Brett said mildly. 'And yes, it was my idea.'

Erin looked at the angry man. 'I don't understand why you're so upset, Jim. I told you last time we met that I was going to stay.'

'I thought it was bravado. I never thought for a moment that you really meant it.'

'Why wouldn't I, Jim?' she asked quietly.

'Because it's damned awkward when we meet— running into each other every time I come here. This is where my friends go, Erin, and I come here too. I stayed away last week because I knew you were here, but I won't stay away forever.'

'You must do as you please.' Erin's tone was composed.

Jim regarded her sullenly. All at once an ugly expression appeared in his eyes. 'You may not want to remain here much longer, Erin. Somehow I don't think you will.'

So saying, he strode away. He walked across the room to the disc jockey, muttered something in the man's ear. Then he joined Priscilla.

A song ended and the music stopped. Hand in hand, Jim and Priscilla walked into the centre of the dance-floor. Guessing what was about to happen, Erin tensed.

'Ladies and gentlemen.' Jim's voice was unnaturally loud and bright. 'I have an announcement. Priscilla and I are engaged.'

There was a burst of applause and cheers rang through the room. Only at Erin and Brett's table, and at Liz and Don's near by, was there silence. Erin was grateful for Brett's hand over hers.

When the applause had quietened, Jim went on speaking. 'We're going to be married as soon as possible.' His arm tightened around Priscilla, but his eyes were on Erin.

More applause, and congratulatory shouts from Jim's friends. The music started once more. On the dance-floor, people resumed their dancing. Jim and Priscilla had seated themselves at a table near the door, and within minutes a waiter had brought them a bottle of champagne.

Withdrawing her hand from Brett's, Erin pushed back her chair and stood up.

'Stay where you are,' he advised quietly. 'Don't play into Jim's hands by running away.'

Erin's lips were set, her eyes steady. 'Do you think I'd give him that satisfaction?' she asked grimly.

Without waiting for an answer, she walked steadily towards the table by the door. Priscilla saw her first. She murmured something to Jim, then they were both watching her. As Erin stopped beside them, Priscilla put a hand on Jim's arm.

'Congratulations,' Erin said.

She had caught them by surprise, she saw, for they did not seem to know how to respond to her. Priscilla's expression was wary, Jim looked angry.

Erin smiled. 'I'm sure you're both very well suited. I hope you'll be happy together.'

Jim seemed about to say something then, but Erin, uncertain how much further she could trust her composure, did not wait to hear his words. Turning, she walked blindly back to her table.

'You're a classy woman, prairie girl,' Brett said, as she sat down, and she saw that his eyes were warm with admiration.

CHAPTER EIGHT

'COME home, Erin.'

'Not yet, Mom.'

'*When*?'

'I can't tell you. It will be a while longer before I have enough money.'

Erin's parents had phoned her once a week since she had been at Hilltop Inn. On this Sunday morning, just a few hours after the dance, Erin had blurted out the news of Jim and Priscilla's engagement. Hearing the unhappiness in her mother's tone, she wondered if she should have been a little more circumspect.

'We'll send you the money, honey,' her mother went on.

But that would strain her parents' resources, Erin knew. After years of battling to make a living on the farm, they were close to retirement and could ill afford such a big expense.

Gently she said, 'I don't want you to do that.'

'You can pay us back when you're able to. Come home, Erin. It must have been bad enough until now, living so near to Jim. But once he's married it can only be a lot worse. Don't put yourself through this trauma, honey,' urged her mother.

Out of the corner of her eye, Erin saw Brett walking into the office, where she had taken the call.

Softly she said, 'I don't want you and Dad worrying about me. I'll be OK, Mom, really, I will.'

'Erin——'

'I have to go now. Talk to you again soon.'

Swept by a wave of homesickness, Erin swallowed hard as she put down the phone. She missed her family more than they would ever know. It had been difficult to say goodbye to them all when she'd left Canada, but at least then she had had a wedding and a new life to look forward to. Now, more than ever, the distance between them seemed unbelievably great.

'Your mother?' Brett asked from behind her.

'Yes. Without thinking, I told her about Jim's engagement, but I wish now that I hadn't. She was so upset by the news that she said she and Dad would send me money for the tickets.'

'What did you say to that?'

'I said no.' Erin lifted her head. 'Even if I felt that my parents could afford it—and as it happens they can't—I will *not* let Jim Saunders intimidate me into leaving before I'm ready to. There's nothing he wants more than to see the back of me. My presence at Hilltop Inn reminds him of his abominable behaviour, and he hates me for that. Well, I won't give him the satisfaction of going. Not yet, anyway.'

Brett's hands went to her shoulders, drawing her towards him. 'Last night I said you had class, but there's more to you than that. You're the bravest woman I know, Erin.'

It felt so good to be close to him. More than anything she wanted to feel his arms around her, to lose herself in his kisses. Not for the first time since she had met Brett, Erin wondered if things would have proceeded differently between them if they'd met in another time, before Jim had disrupted her life and filled her mind with doubts and cynicism.

'I have plans for today,' Brett told her.

Erin tilted her head so that she could look at him. 'Plans?' she queried.

'It's time you learned how to drive.'

'I can drive, Brett,' she told him.

'You've never driven on the left side of the road. Once you've had some practice, there's a spare car here which you could use.'

'I'd like that very much,' Erin said eagerly. 'It would mean I could drive into town whenever I need supplies, instead of depending on other people to buy them for me. I have an international driver's licence which is valid for a year, so I wouldn't even have to take a test.'

'Unless you decide to make this your permanent home, of course, in which case you'd have to pass a new test.'

Brett was so close to her that she could see the length of his lashes and the golden lights in eyes that were deep and warm and speculative.

'Why would I do that?' she asked, a little breathlessly.

'Why don't you tell me?' he asked softly.

The warmth of the hard body just inches from hers was unnerving. Even though there was a part of her that would have welcomed his kisses seconds earlier, she moved out of his hands and took a few steps away from him. She saw his lips turn up slightly, as if he understood her sudden need for space, and was amused by it.

'You know that I'm planning to go back home as soon as I have enough money—I keep telling you that.' Her throat was so dry that it was an effort to speak.

'Ah.'

Only one word. But her eyes slid away from his as she asked, 'Where are we going to do this practising?'

'Somewhere quiet, where you can get the feel of the left side of the road.'

'The *wrong* side,' she said, pretending a lightness she was far from feeling.

Brett laughed. 'The correct side, we like to think, but we won't quibble about it. Why don't you go and fetch your licence, and I'll meet you in ten minutes by the garages?'

Erin walked quickly to her rondavel. It didn't take her more than a few seconds to pick up the wallet where she kept all her pieces of identification. Slinging a tapestry bag over her shoulder, she was about to make for the door when her feet took her to the mirror instead. She stared at her reflection—at eyes that were unnaturally bright, at cheeks that were flushed above their new tan, at lips that trembled. This was the face Brett had seen. There was no way he could not have sensed her excitement.

Reaching the garages, a collection of buildings not far from the stables, Erin found that Brett had already taken out a small red Honda.

'I'll drive her out of the grounds,' he said. 'After that you can take over.'

Erin's eyes sparkled. 'Less risky that way?'

He grinned back at her. 'You said that, I didn't. Climb in, Erin.'

Leaving the hotel, he drove a little way along the highway. When they came to a secondary road, he turned in and stopped the car.

'Now then,' he said, 'let's see what you can do, Erin.'

He opened his door and walked around the car. Seconds later she was seated behind the wheel, Brett in the passenger seat.

'I forgot to ask if you were familiar with automatic transmission,' he said.

'Actually, my car at home isn't very different from this one,' she told him. 'It's taken me over ice and snow without mishap.'

'This one just needs to take you over tar and the occasional sandy stretch, so you should have no problems.'

Erin ran her hands over the steering-wheel, and tested the brake and the accelerator with her right foot. Confident that she knew what she was about, she turned the key and released the brake.

On the day that Brett had given her a ride to the Shatobi plantation, the sensation of being on the left side of the road had been strange and a little dizzying. Though Erin had got used to travelling on the left side since then, she found out very quickly that the experience of being a passenger was quite different from that of being a driver.

Beside her, she heard the low sound of Brett's laughter.

'A joke?' she asked, without taking her eyes from the road.

'The scowl on your face, for one thing.'

'I'll have you know that I'm concentrating.'

'Is that what you're doing? And the way you're holding on to the wheel—it won't run away from you even if you don't grip it so tightly. Relax, Erin.'

'Try driving on the wrong side of the road yourself some day, and see how you like it. My God, Brett, there's a car!' she exclaimed suddenly.

'I see it. You're doing fine, Erin.'

The approaching car was driving fast. To Erin, accustomed to seeing vehicles coming towards her from a different perspective, it seemed as if they had to collide. Her grip on the wheel tightened, and her teeth bit down hard on her lower lip. The car came nearer, it was just a few feet away from them now. Beads of perspiration stood on her forehead. The car passed her. Seconds later it was out of sight in her rear mirror.

'Well done,' Brett said.

'I *did* it!' she exclaimed.

'You certainly did. Keep going, Erin. And relax.'

It was easier after that. Erin had always enjoyed driving, and as she started to get the feel of the road she began to enjoy herself once again.

'Nothing to it,' she said after a while.

'You'll have to think about what you're doing when you turn a corner,' Brett told her.

'Will that be a problem?'

'Not if you concentrate. Remember which side of the road you should be on. A right turn is the big one here, a left turn the small one.'

She threw him a cheeky grin. 'I'll remember that, teacher.'

He grinned back at her. 'See that you do.'

The miles vanished beneath the wheels. More cars approached, and once a van pulling a caravan. Erin tightened the first few times, but after that she relaxed. She even summoned the confidence to pass a slow-moving car.

She had been driving for more than half an hour when Brett said, 'About two miles from here you'll see a road going off to the right. 'We'll make a turn there.'

Erin slowed the car as she saw the signpost in the distance. She was relaxed as she came out of the turn— only to grow rigid seconds later as a jeep topped a rise and came directly towards her.

Reaching quickly for the wheel, Brett jerked it to the left.

When the jeep had passed, Erin slowed the car to a halt at the side of the road. She was shuddering violently.

'Oh, lord, Brett . . .' she muttered.

'It's OK, Erin,' he said gently.

'That was close.'

'You weren't thinking as you turned—that's why you found yourself on the wrong side of the road.'

'I can't go on,' she whispered.

'Yes, you can. You were becoming too confident, but you won't make that particular mistake again. Next time you'll be concentrating.'

His arm went around her shoulders, and slowly her shuddering lessened. A few minutes later she was able to drive further.

Fifteen miles or so down the bumpy farm road, Brett said, 'Turn left at the windmill.'

This time Erin concentrated as she turned. After years of driving, her instinct was to hug the right side of the road; but her intellect reminded her to keep to the left, and she was able to complete the turn successfully.

'There's my Erin!' said Brett. 'I knew you could do it. Stop at the cabin in the trees.'

'Where are we?' she asked.

'You'll see.'

The cabin turned out to be Brett's private retreat, the place to which he came when he wanted to be alone. Following him inside, Erin found herself in a room with woven rugs and wicker furniture, and shelves holding books and records and tapes. In a corner was a collection of fishing-rods.

'I love it!' she exclaimed.

'I thought you might. This is a special place, Erin. I'm choosy about the people I bring here.'

There was an intense look in the dark eyes. Erin's heart quickened.

'Wait here,' Brett said.

He walked out of the door and the cabin seemed suddenly empty, as if the books and the records and the fishing-rods in the corner were as nothing without the vibrant personality of their owner.

He was back a minute later with a basket. 'A picnic,' he announced, in response to Erin's mystified look. 'You didn't see it because it was in the boot of the car. The chef assembled it for us before we left the hotel.'

Together they unpacked the picnic meal and set it out on a rug by the window. Apart from a selection of sandwiches, tiny pastries and a few fat peaches, there was also a bottle of wine.

'Do you make a habit of treating your students to delicious meals with their driving lessons?' Erin teased, as Brett pulled out a chair and waited for her to sit down.

'Only the beautiful ones, with the sexiest bodies and the most kissable lips.'

The words were lightly spoken, and obviously intended as a joke. No reason why they should set desire flaming like a veld-fire in Erin's loins.

'For the record,' Brett added, his tone as light as before, 'there have been no other students.'

'It wouldn't have been any of my concern if there had been.'

'I thought you might like to know.'

Brett uncorked the wine. When he had poured it, he handed Erin a glass.

'A toast,' he said, lifting his glass. 'To safe and happy driving.'

'I endorse the safety bit,' she said fervently.

He threw her a maddening grin. 'You'll do just fine, Erin. You're a good driver, and that one mistake will keep you concentrating from now on.'

They sipped their wine, then he motioned to her to help herself to some food. She took a peach and a small sandwich, and though she was not hungry she pretended to eat.

Then Brett said, 'Erin—did you mind very much?'

They had not spoken at all about the events of the previous evening, but she knew, without asking, what he meant. 'Jim and Priscilla?'

'Yes.'

'It hurts to be humiliated, Brett. And in front of so many people who must have known about my own engagement to Jim. It wasn't easy to wish them well, especially when I could cheerfully have strangled them both.'

'It had to be difficult,' Brett acknowledged. 'But that wasn't really my question.'

Erin put down the wine glass she'd been holding and looked at Brett with troubled eyes. 'You want to know if I have any feelings left for Jim.'

'Yes.'

'I'm over him—I know that now. I'm even beginning to wonder whether I was ever in love with him in the first place. How do I know that what I felt for him wasn't infatuation all the time?'

'Do you think you'd have got over him quite so quickly if it had been love?'

Erin looked at Brett, caught by the odd intensity in his tone. She saw the hunger in his eyes, and suddenly the breath caught in her throat and every nerve was throbbing inside her.

'Do you really believe that you loved Jim?' he asked softly.

'Maybe not.' Erin's voice was unsteady.

A muscle moved in the strong jaw. 'That's an admission you wouldn't have made a few weeks ago.'

'I wish I could be sure...'

'You're going to have to learn to go with your feelings, Erin.' His voice was husky now. 'As I intend going with mine.'

Putting down his glass, he reached for her hands. His eyes holding hers, defying them to shift from his gaze, he brought her hands up to his mouth. His tongue played in the palm of one hand, then the other, sensuously, provocatively, sending sparks of heat cascading through her body.

'I'm going to make love to you,' he said, his voice even softer now.

'Brett...' His name emerged on a raw throat.

'Don't fight it, sweetheart. Let it happen.'

He straightened from a sitting position to kneeling, and pulled her up with him. His arms went around her, and her neck bent back as his lips came down on hers. His kisses were hard, demanding, more passionate than they had ever been. Arching herself against him, revelling in the hardness of his hips against hers, Erin kissed him back with an abandon born of need. Tiny animal sounds escaped her, but she did not know she was making them. There was only Brett, and the sweetness of his lips, the exploration of his tongue, the primitive pulsing heat of her body. She felt alive and female and desirable; wanting more, needing more.

When Brett slipped a hand beneath her knees and straightened her legs to a lying position, she was yielding, pliant, helping him, for what he wanted she wanted too. The woven rug was rough beneath her head and neck, but she did not notice it as she held out her arms to him. He bent over her and unbuttoned the top buttons of her blouse, then his hand slid inwards, over her warm breasts. His fingers cupped her nipples, and she felt them harden beneath his touch. Then he opened the blouse all the way, and began to draw long brush-strokes with his tongue between her breasts, around them, up to her throat, and down along the smoothness of her stomach. Erin's head arched back and her eyes closed as each flick of the wicked tongue kindled fresh fire along nerves that were already so raw that she did not know how she could bear the hunger which was growing second by second inside her. Only the merest thread held her to sanity, and even that was threatening to snap.

Her heart thundered in her ears so that she barely heard Brett when he sat back and said, 'Look at me, Erin.'

'I can't...'

'I have to know—is this what you want, sweetheart?'

She did not stop to think. The decisions she had made in more rational moments were far from her mind now.

'*Yes*!' she whispered.

'You're so beautiful, Erin,' he groaned. 'So sexy, so utterly lovely. I've been wanting to do this with you for so long.'

She wanted him to kiss her again, and she wanted to kiss him too. Lifting her arms, she reached for his shoulders and pulled him down against her. His face blotted out her vision, and she revelled in the dark hardness around her, lost in an ecstasy of desire that was like nothing she had ever known, ever dreamed of. When he sat up she reached for him again, feeling lost suddenly, abandoned, her mouth seeking his. But he was undressing her, drawing her blouse from her shoulders, her bra, sliding her trousers from her hips. And then she was undressing him too, her fingers sliding along hard bone, gasping with pleasure as he stroked her hips and her breasts.

'I want you so much,' he said raggedly, as he lay down beside her and gathered her to him.

'I want you too, Brett.'

'You do know—don't you?'

'Know what?' she asked, through a haze.

'That what you felt for Jim couldn't possibly have been love.'

Through her hunger, through the urgency of her need, the words got through to her. She lay still in his arms.

'You do know, don't you, Erin? Why don't you admit it?'

She knew what he wanted her to say. She longed to say the one word he needed to hear.

'Erin?' he urged.

'I'm not sure what it was,' she whispered.

'It was infatuation—it had to be.'

'I'd like to say it was that, but I don't know.'

Brett sat up. 'My God, Erin!' he exclaimed.

Feeling bereft, she reached for him, trying to draw him back to her, but his body was stiff in her hands.

'This was a mistake,' he said harshly.

'No!'

'You're still not ready for this. I thought you were, but I was wrong.'

Her body was on fire. 'How can you say that?' she gasped.

'You're still too unclear about your feelings for Jim.'

'What do they have to do with us?' she cried painfully.

'Everything. You told me once that if you were to be attracted to another man after Jim it could only be on the rebound.'

'I did say that,' she whispered.

'I don't intend to be that man, Erin. I can't be. However much I might want you.'

She stared at him, distraught and frustrated, unable to counter what he was saying, knowing only how much she wanted him to come back into her arms.

'When you're clear about your feelings for Jim, you'll be ready for this. Only then.'

'But I want you, Brett...'

'When—*if*—you know how you really feel, tell me. In the meantime, get dressed, Erin.'

She opened her mouth to speak, to tell him that the feelings she had once had for Jim—whether they'd been love or not—were irrelevant to what was happening now, in the cabin. She needed him to make love to her.

But Brett had already turned away. Roughly, deliberately, he was pulling on his trousers and then his shirt.

All at once Erin became aware of her own naked state on the floor. Feeling hurt and cheap, she sat up and gathered her clothes. Holding them in front of her—not that it mattered, for Brett was not looking at her—she walked into the bathroom where she could get dressed in private.

Without thinking, she paused in front of the mirror. Earlier that morning she had seen a reflection of anticipation and excitement, but the face she saw now shocked her. Her eyes were hazy with desire, her lips were red and swollen. She looked like a wanton. Turning on the tap, she began to throw water over her face. The water was icy, a shock to her system, but welcome too. Fiercely, savagely, she splashed her face, her throat, her body. And when tears came, tears of rage and of frustration, she was certain that no tell-tale signs of her emotion remained.

Only then, head held high, did she walk back into the room where Brett was waiting for her. He was standing at the window, his body rigid with some inner battle of his own. She did not ask him what was bothering him. She did not care. She only knew that in the space of a short time she had been humiliated first by one man, then by another.

If Erin's personal life was a turmoil of frustration, the gift store was more successful than ever. A farming couple were going to be celebrating their golden wedding anniversary and their children had decided to throw them a surprise party. Although the three daughters of the family had cooked and baked all their lives, none was versed in speciality cakes.

Erin listened quietly as the women told her about their plans. They'd thought about a really grand cake, they said, one which would take pride of place on the party table. Erin showed them her illustrated baking books, and they spent more than an hour looking at pictures before deciding on the cake they wanted—round, and topped with a golden cornucopia filled with small gold-wrapped chocolate coins.

The party order did not end there. Two elaborate tortes were to be placed on either side of the main cake, and for each guest there was to be a little bag of Erin's chocolates.

Erin began to plan for the party the same day. When she had drawn up a list of all the things she would need, she took the car Brett had put at her disposal and drove to town to shop for ingredients. Driving was easy now, with only the turns requiring special concentration.

When she was not in the store, she was in the kitchen. There were days when she was so tired by the time she went to bed that her head throbbed and her back and feet ached. But she did not regret accepting the order. She was enjoying the success of her career, and apart from the fact that her bank account was about to receive a hefty jolt she was glad that she was too busy to think about Brett.

She saw him now and then, on her way to the kitchen, or when she took off a few minutes for a quick walk through the gardens. Once she looked up as she was serving a customer and found Brett watching her from the doorway. He gave her a polite smile of recognition, but when she looked up again he was gone. The shortest of encounters, yet long enough to unnerve her.

Late one afternoon she saw him at the pool. The setting sun gave a golden sheen to the bronzed body, all hard limbs and smooth muscle, and as Erin watched him dive into the water she felt a running of heat in her veins. When he had swum a few lengths, swiftly, streamlined as a fish, he stopped at the far end of the pool and raised an arm in greeting.

Erin waved back briefly, then turned and walked quickly away from the water. Desire was a throbbing in her loins and her face was hot.

The golden anniversary came and went. Erin's cakes were praised by all who saw them, and there was talk of more orders.

A few days after the party, Brett appeared once more at Erin's Place.

'Your fame is spreading,' he said. 'I just received an order for another cake.'

'What kind of cake, Brett?'

'A wedding cake.'

'For whom?'

Brett did not answer immediately. Erin looked at him curiously. His eyes were hooded yet watchful.

Suddenly she knew the answer to her question. 'Jim?' 'Yes.'

'You took an order for Jim and Priscilla's wedding cake?'

'That's right,' he agreed.

'Tell me this is a joke, Brett.'

'It's no joke, Erin.'

'I suppose I don't need to ask where the wedding will be held.'

'At Hilltop Inn,' he acknowledged. 'There's one more thing you should know. I agreed that you'd be on hand to supervise the wedding reception.'

Her muscles were tight as she looked at him. 'I can't believe you'd do such a thing.'

'We're running a business here. We don't turn down orders because we dislike the people involved.'

'*We*, Brett? Erin's Place is my business.'

'Not quite,' he said. 'It's part of the hotel. I employ you.'

'Thank you for reminding me.' Her lips were dry and stiff. 'But I could refuse to do this, Brett.'

'No, Erin, you can't.'

'Why not?' she asked.

'Hilltop Inn has a reputation to uphold, and that would suffer if we backed down once we'd given our word.'

She stared at him, unable to believe what she was hearing. It was as if she and Brett had become strangers, their only association one of employer and employee, as if the wonder of their lovemaking had never occurred. She felt utterly betrayed.

'Are you saying that you'll fire me if I don't do the baking?' she demanded.

'Draw your own conclusions,' he drawled.

'It never occurred to me that you could be so cruel.'

Something flickered in the dark eyes, but he remained silent.

'I guess you realise that if I didn't need the money so badly I'd walk out of Hilltop Inn this minute and be on my way back to Canada tomorrow.'

Still Brett was silent.

'The problem is,' Erin said, 'I don't have enough saved up yet. Though I will have soon.'

'Does that mean you will do the baking?'

'It means you've won, Brett,' she said flatly.

'I hope I have.' There was a gleam in his eyes now. 'I really hope I have, Erin.'

She bit down on her lip in anger. 'Don't you think you could have spoken to me before agreeing to this order?' she asked quietly.

'You said you were over Jim.'

'So I am.'

'Then baking for his wedding shouldn't mean anything to you.'

'You must be very insensitive if you believe that,' she said bitterly. 'It's true I don't care about Jim any more. But his wedding, and to the very woman I found in his bed a few days before my own wedding was to take place—now that's something else again. Did you consider my feelings at all when you said yes to them? Did you think what it would do to me to bake these cakes? To watch Jim and Priscilla get married?'

'Why don't you tell me what it will do to you, Erin?' There was such an odd expression in his eyes.

'I'm not sure you care,' she said, flinging the words at him.

'I'd hardly be asking the question if I didn't.'

'I'll let you know the answer after the wedding,' she told him.

'I wish you'd do that,' he said.

He was at the door when Erin asked, 'How do you know I won't put rat poison in the cake?'

He turned back. 'I don't,' he said, and she saw that his eyes were sparkling.

CHAPTER NINE

'ERIN...?'

Erin was at the far end of the store, arranging a pyramid of jams and honeys which one of her local suppliers had brought in the previous day. She loved the creativity involved in finding new and attractive ways of displaying her merchandise. She especially looked forward to the visits of the farming women who arrived with the jars they had pickled and canned, and who almost always had time for coffee and a chat. Every day Erin was making new friends.

At the sound of her name she turned. In a moment she stiffened.

Jim and Priscilla were standing by the long table. They were holding hands. Their expressions were similar, a mixture of aggression and bravado together with a distinct measure of discomfort.

Two days had passed since Brett had made his bombshell announcement. Apart from a few token words, Erin had not spoken to him since then. She was still furious at what she regarded as his betrayal, but Brett seemed to take her outrage in his stride. Certainly he did nothing to apologise for the position he had put her in.

Jim looked at his fiancée, as if waiting for her to speak first.

'We're here to talk about the wedding cake,' Priscilla said.

Once Erin had accepted the inevitability of her situation, she had made up her mind to handle it with dignity. 'I was expecting you.'

'You were?'. The day was cool, the sky overcast with a promise of rain, yet Jim's face was flushed.

Erin treated him to a polite look. 'Brett informed me of the arrangements you'd made with him. I have a book with illustrations you might want to look at. It could give you some ideas.'

Jim was looking uncomfortable.

'Erin...' Dropping Priscilla's hand, he took a step closer towards the girl he had once been engaged to.

'Sweetheart!' Priscilla said.

Jim ignored her protest. 'I'm sorry.'

'For what?' Erin's tone was impersonal.

'The thing is, I told you from the outset to go back to Canada—or at least to work elsewhere. I said it more than once.'

'That's right, Jim, you did.'

'If you'd listened to me, this wouldn't have happened. You wouldn't be the one baking our cake.'

'But it has happened, and I am going to be baking for you, so why don't we just make the best of it?'

'You're a cool fish, aren't you, Erin?' The momentary discomfort was gone from Jim's eyes.

'Am I?'

'That's something I didn't realise when we met at the rodeo—or afterwards. I don't think you were ever in love with me.'

'I think you'd like to believe that I wasn't,' Erin said. 'Because if that was true it would make this whole fiasco so much easier for you to deal with, wouldn't it, Jim?'

Jim hesitated. 'If you were really so broken-hearted about finding me with Priscilla, you wouldn't have re-

mained here. You'd have found a way of leaving, found
a job elsewhere, no matter what.'

'Maybe you're right,' she agreed.

'I had a different impression of you when we met,
Erin.'

'My impressions of you were different too,' she said
calmly. 'Perhaps it's just as well that things turned out
the way they did, because we would never have been
happy together in the long run. I know that now.'

Jim's look of anger gave her a moment of satisfaction.

'To get back to the business in hand,' she said briskly,
as she opened a drawer and took out a large, glossy-
bound book, 'you can take this home with you if you
like. When you've made up your minds about the cake
you want, let me know and we'll discuss it.'

'Actually, we need more than a wedding cake,' Priscilla
said.

Her left hand was on Jim's arm now. Erin's eyes went
to the ring which she herself had once worn with such
pride. Then she looked back at the woman who had had
no scruples about starting an affair with a man who had
been about to marry someone else.

'What do you have in mind?' she asked.

'Something fancy for the party.'

'Pastries? Tortes?'

'Can you make fancy things, Erin?'

Erin's voice was professionally pleasant. 'Just as fancy
as you like.'

For which Jim and Priscilla would make handsome
payment, she decided grimly. With the wedding over,
she hoped to have enough money to pay for her journey
home.

'Did Brett also tell you that we want you to supervise
the reception?' Jim asked.

'He did. But I can't help wondering, wouldn't it bother you to have me there—me of all people, Jim?'

He threw her an insolent look. 'It was your choice to go into this business, Erin.'

'That's right, it was my own choice,' she agreed.

He looked a little taken aback for a moment. Then he said, 'Can we take it you'll do it?'

'You'll pay for the service, Jim, but yes, if that's what you want, I can do it.'

'So,' Brett said, when he met Erin outside the main building later in the day, 'I believe Jim and Priscilla paid you a visit this morning.'

'They did,' she told him.

'How did it go?'

She threw him a challenging look. 'I didn't mention the rat poison, if that's what you're asking.'

'Ah.' His eyes sparkled.

'Nor did I throw a tantrum.'

'That's my Erin.'

'Not your Erin, Brett. Just the employee who runs Erin's Place for you.'

His expression was difficult to read. 'Do I sense that you've accepted the situation?'

'Thanks to your insensitivity, I didn't have an alternative, did I?' Thoughtfully she added, 'There is one good thing that will come out of this.'

'What's that, Erin?' asked Brett.

'When I add my commission on the wedding baking to what I've already saved, I should have enough to pay for my flights.'

'Still determined to leave here?'

'More than ever,' she assured him.

Brett reached out a hand to touch her cheek. Erin took a quick step away from him, and, after a moment, his hand dropped to his side.

'Erin...' he said.

'No!'

'How can you refuse me when you don't even know what I was going to say?'

'Whatever it is, I don't want to hear it.'

'Spend the day with me,' he said. 'I'll get the horses saddled, and a picnic basket made up.'

'So that you can make love to me again?' The words emerged before she could think about them.

'Is that what you'd like?' he said softly. 'Do you want to go back to the cabin?'

It appalled Erin to realise quite how much she wanted it. Just the sight of the rugged face brought back so many memories. She felt weak with wanting Brett—even now, when he had betrayed her.

'No,' she said harshly. 'I'm sorry we went to the cabin that day. I wish I could wipe everything that happened there from my mind.'

'Finding that's not easy?'

'Easier than you might like to think, Brett. You see, I despise you so intensely for making me bake for Jim's wedding that I can only remember what happened between us with revulsion.'

Without waiting for an answer, she turned her head and walked away.

A few days later Jim and Priscilla were back in the store. When they had shown Erin the picture of the cake they had chosen, and discussed a few tortes and pastries for the reception, they wanted to know how much her baking would cost them.

This was one instance where Erin had made no attempt to find ways of keeping her prices low. She gave them her figures squarely, and saw Jim flinch.

'That much?' he asked, looking a little pale.

'That much,' she answered firmly.

'It's steep. A lot steeper than I'd expected.'

'If it's more than you want to spend, perhaps Priscilla would like to do the baking herself,' Erin said, very politely.

She saw them look at each other.

'The stuff had better be good,' Priscilla muttered then.

In the daylight, the woman was not as attractive as she had been at the first dance. Her eyes had a sullen expression, as if she was constantly bored with life, and discontented. Erin, who suspected that Jim's engagement might have been an act of bravado meant to hurt her, wondered how happy the marriage would be once the first novelty had faded.

'My work is professional,' she said quietly.

Another look passed between the betrothed pair.

'We seem to have no option,' Jim shrugged. 'We may as well talk.'

When Jim and Priscilla had gone, Erin made herself a cup of strong coffee. Then she sat down with pen and paper and began to make a list of everything she would need. Now that the wedding and her own part in it had become fact, she could not wait to get on with it. The sooner it was over, the sooner she could begin making her own plans.

Putting down her decorating tube, Erin passed the back of her hand across her damp forehead. She had lost count of the time she had spent on her feet that day. There was not a part of her body that did not ache. On a far counter stood the wedding cake; on another counter was a platter of tiny ornamental pastries. Now she was busy putting the finishing touches to the tortes for the wedding reception, which was to take place the next day.

'Still busy?' someone asked.

Erin spun around. 'Why, Brett! You startled me. I didn't hear you come in.'

'No wonder—you looked lost in thought. Don't you know it's well past the witching hour, Erin? Just as well you don't depend on a coach for a ride back to your rondavel—it would have turned into a pumpkin long ago.'

She gave him a tired smile. 'Just as well. What are you doing here?'

'I noticed the light in the kitchen, and came to investigate. Isn't it time you called it a night?'

'I intend to, just as soon as I'm done here,' she assured him.

'Quite a job you took on, Erin.'

Too tired to be really angry, she felt a small sense of outrage nevertheless. '*You* took on, Brett,' she retorted.

An expression came and went in his eyes—something oddly like pain, though not quite that.

'Why did you do it, Brett?' she asked curiously.

'I had my reasons.'

'Profit, obviously. You saw a chance to make some money, and you couldn't resist it.'

'Is that what you think, Erin?'

'What else, if not that?'

Instead of answering, Brett lifted a damp tendril of hair from her forehead and wound it around his forefinger. He was so close to her that the familiar male smell of his body touched her nostrils.

'Don't,' she said hoarsely.

Still with the hair wrapped around his finger, he stroked her damp face with his thumb. Tired as Erin was, the movement made her tremble. Briefly she closed her eyes. A second later, remembering where she was, and what had brought her here, she snapped open her eyes, glared at Brett, then stepped away from him. He released her hair without protest.

'So you think my motive was profit,' he said.

'It's the only one I can think of.'

'If you happen to think of another, I'll be interested in hearing about it.'

He glanced around him then, at the tortes on the counter, at the pastries and the wedding cake, at all the dishes and utensils which Erin had used.

'How much longer will you be?' he asked.

'I have no idea.'

'You look exhausted.'

Her eyes burned with fatigue and her head was beginning to throb, but she would not give him the satisfaction of telling him that.

'I'll be fine,' she said.

'What do you still have left to do?'

'The tortes need a few final touches, then I have to clean up. Basile will throw a fit if he walks into his kitchen—his *kingdom*—tomorrow, and finds a dish soiled or out of place. Couldn't you have employed someone a little less temperamental?'

Brett grinned. 'Basile is such a fine chef that I'm prepared to put up with a bit of temperament.'

He moved away, and Erin turned her attention back to her creations. She was surprised when Brett reappeared at her side a minute later, holding a glass.

'Iced lemonade,' he informed her. 'Sit down and drink it.'

'I don't have time.'

'You need a break. Have a few sips, then you can go on working.'

She looked at him, saw the firmness in his face, sensed the authority in his manner. She wanted him to leave her alone to finish her work, but she was too tired to argue with him.

'If I drink this, then will you go away and leave me to finish?'

He grinned at her again, looking not the least bit tired himself. Taking her by the hand, he led her to a chair and motioned to her to sit down. She tried to take the glass from his fingers and saw that her own fingers were trembling. Brett must have seen it too, for he held on to the glass, brought it to her lips and said, quite gently, 'Drink, Erin.'

She tried not to be touched by the gesture. Brett would have to be a monster if he was totally indifferent to her weary state.

'You'd think I was a baby,' she muttered.

'Just a very tired baker. Drink, Erin.'

Unable to protest further, she let her lips open on the rim of the glass. The lemonade was cold, slightly sour rather than too sweet.

'Good?' Brett asked.

'Delicious. Just what I needed to survive,' she admitted gratefully. She stood up. 'If I don't force myself to go on, I'll probably fall asleep on the chair. Thanks for the refreshment, Brett. Please, go now, and leave me to it.'

Without another look at him, she returned to her work. Picking up her decorating tube, she began to trail a thin spiral of red frosting beside a brown one. In normal circumstances the movement would not have been difficult, but, weary as she was now, it needed her full concentration.

Vaguely she was aware of Brett's continued presence in the kitchen. The red spiral finished, she looked around, about to tell him that he was disturbing her, but the words died on her lips when she saw that he had stacked the dirty dishes and was now carrying them to the sink.

'I thought you were leaving the kitchen, Brett,' she said.

'Did I say that?'

'I asked you to go.'

'And I decided to stay.'

'You really don't have to clean up for me,' she insisted.

'Perhaps I want to.'

'I don't need your help, Brett.'

'Still mad at me, are you?'

'Of course I am. What you did was unforgivable. So why don't you just put down those dishes and go?'

'I intend to finish what I started,' he told her.

'The boss helping the employee?'

'You like to emphasise the difference between us, don't you, Erin?'

'I'm saying it as it is.'

'As you'd like to think it is.'

'As it is,' Erin said firmly. 'You didn't give me any choice when it came to baking for Jim's wedding.'

'Erin——'

'Just as long as your help doesn't mean a chop in my commission,' she taunted.

He burst out laughing at that. 'I won't diddle you out of a single cent, if that's what you're thinking. But enough talk for now, it's back to work for us both.'

Half an hour later, when Erin had finally finished decorating the tortes, she looked around her with gratitude. The kitchen was so clean that Basile would have to use a magnifying glass to find a speck of dirt anywhere.

'Thanks, Brett,' she said.

'The pleasure was mine.' Incredibly, he looked as if he meant it.

'Well—goodnight, then.'

'You can say that when we get to your rondavel.'

'No payment for services rendered, Brett,' Erin said firmly.

'You're perfectly safe—tonight.' His eyes gleamed. 'I may be a monster in your eyes, Erin, but even I wouldn't force my attentions on a woman who's so weary that she'd find it difficult to get her feet to take her from this kitchen to her bed.'

Without warning, he closed the distance between them and scooped her up into his arms.

'Put me down!' she snapped.

'You're exhausted.'

'I'm perfectly able to walk on my own.'

'You can hardly stand on your feet,' he told her.

'I don't want you to do this, Brett.'

'Hush,' he said. 'We don't want to wake anyone. Try and forget for a few minutes what a despicable character I am, and be still while I carry you.'

So saying, he lifted an elbow to switch off the light, then walked along the passage towards the door that led out of the building.

As if Erin were weightless, he strode easily along the dimly lit path that led towards the rondavels. Erin knew she should not let him get away with it, but she was too tired to argue any longer. More than that, she found she did not want to. The feel of Brett's rough sweater was bliss against her hot cheek. His heartbeat was exciting against her throat. Insanely, she wished the path was never-ending so that she could remain wrapped forever in Brett's arms. Leaning her face into his sweater, she closed her eyes.

She did not know they had arrived at her rondavel until she heard him say, 'Where's your key?'

She opened her eyes and lifted her head to look at him, wondering, a little too late, if he had noticed how she had nuzzled herself against his chest.

In the light of the lamp shining above the door, she could see his eyes, deep-set and watchful beneath long lashes; the strong column of his throat; the lips that were so sensuous that she wished he would kiss her. It would be so easy to reach up and touch his face; to say, 'Stay with me tonight.'

But she made herself put her hand in her pocket and take out the key.

Somehow he managed to hold her steady with one arm, while with his free hand he opened the door. Erin tried to stand, but Brett held her firmly. Pushing open the door of the rondavel with his foot, he carried her inside and put her down on the bed.

'Where do you keep whatever it is you wear at night, Erin?'

'I can manage,' she said.

'*Where*, Erin? Or do you sleep naked?'

She nodded her head in the direction of a bureau. 'Top drawer. But Brett...'

The protest came too late, for he was already walking across the room. Erin's breath quickened as she watched him touching her most personal apparel.

He walked back to the bed holding a white nightgown trimmed with lace. 'This it?' he asked.

The flimsy garment looked incongruous in the big hands of the man. It was almost as if Erin's soft skin were in his fingers, waiting to be caressed.

She suppressed a shiver. 'Yes, thank you.'

'It's so small, so... delicate.'

'It was part of my trousseau,' she whispered.

Brett looked at her a long moment. In the dim light it was impossible to read his eyes.

'I see,' he said then.

'Give it to me, Brett.'

'I'd like to help you put it on, Erin.'

'Things wouldn't end there if you did that,' she warned.

'And you don't want me to make love to you.' It was a statement rather than a question.

'No.' Her throat was so dry that it felt raw.

He stared down at her as she lay, quite still, looking up at him. For several heart-stopping seconds Erin wondered whether he meant to lie down beside her. If he tried to make love to her, she doubted if she had the will to stop him.

Something moved in his throat as he said, 'You know what I want.'

'Brett...'

'It's all right.' His voice had gone flat. 'I'll leave you now.'

He strode across the room and the door closed behind him. Erin stared at it for at least a minute. She felt bereft.

The strident sound of the alarm clock was obscene in the dim room.

'No!' Erin protested weakly, eyes closed as she groped for the clock. It did not seem possible that it was time to get up; she felt as if she had just got to bed minutes earlier. Finding the knob at the back of the clock, she pressed it, silenced the sound, and buried her face in the pillow.

The wake-up call from Liz came ten minutes later. 'Time to get up, Erin.'

'Leave me alone and let me sleep,' Erin pleaded.

'Get to bed late?' Liz asked compassionately.

'Don't ask!'

'That late? I'm sorry to wake you, but you said you wanted to make an early start today.'

The wedding... Wide awake suddenly, Erin murmured her thanks to Liz and put down the phone. By midnight, the wedding would be over. Life would become normal again. And then she remembered that after tomorrow she would have enough money to pay for her journey home. Lips tight suddenly, she pushed the blanket from her bed.

The day proceeded at a quick pace after that. When the last of the hotel guests had finished their breakfast, the doors of the dining-room were closed to the public and the preparations for the wedding reception were begun.

Erin forgot her fatigue as she supervised the layout of the tables and the settings. One of the gardeners arrived with huge bunches of dew-wet flowers. Erin made one big arrangement for the main table, and filled small vases for the individual tables. Often she consulted the lists she had made. There had to be a microphone for the speeches, a place for the band; a table for the wedding cake, and another for the presents.

Now and then Brett looked into the room. 'You're as successful an organiser as you are a baker,' he said once. 'Ever thought of catering professionally?'

Erin's hostility towards him had faded somewhat since the previous night. 'No, I've never considered it,' she said with a smile.

'Perhaps you should. I could see people flocking to Hilltop Inn for festive parties.'

'You may be right, Brett, but you'd have to find someone else to take charge of the catering. I won't be here more than a week or two after this.'

'How I keep forgetting,' Brett drawled.

The wedding itself was to take place in the hotel garden. As hours passed, and the ceremony drew closer, Erin experienced a feeling of dread. Though she had known for some time that she had no feelings left for Jim, it could still be an ordeal to watch him getting married to the woman who had caused her so much unhappiness.

She could have missed the ceremony had there not been things she had to supervise there too. Guests began to arrive; they stood in groups in the garden, while waiters walked among them with canapés and drinks. It was up to Erin to ensure that everything went smoothly.

Wearing a raw silk dress which flattered both her face and her figure, she moved easily through the gardens. Now and then a pointed look and a whispered remark would be directed her way. It was obvious that many of the guests knew who she was, and what her place in the bridegroom's life had been.

Suddenly, not two feet away from her, there was Jim, boyishly handsome in a grey suit with a carnation in his lapel. Their eyes held for a moment. Jim's gaze was the first to waver. Reddening, he turned his head and walked on.

The guests took their places. The pianist began to play the Wedding March, and all heads turned as the bride, wearing an off-the-shoulder white dress, came walking along the path on her father's arm.

Erin watched Priscilla take her place beside Jim. She listened to the minister's words, and heard the bride and the groom exchange their vows.

When the minister said, 'You may kiss the bride,' Jim lifted Priscilla's veil and she put her arms around his neck. Their kiss lasted a long time.

Nothing stirred in Erin. Watching her erstwhile fiancé in the arms of his bride, she felt no pang of sadness, not a single flicker of regret. Throughout the ceremony she was nothing more than a bystander; curious, interested, no more than that.

The music resumed as the bridal couple, hand in hand now, turned to their guests. There was much hugging and kissing, and people began to throw confetti.

'Are you all right?' asked a voice at Erin's side.

She looked up at Brett. Wearing a suit, for once, he looked even more austere than usual. In his face there was none of Jim's youthful charm. Brett was all man— tough, confident, demanding of himself and of others, aware of what he wanted in life. He was also sexy, exciting, and so attractive that the woman who loved him would never have eyes for anyone else. There could be no other man who would be able to touch sides with Brett Mallory.

'Erin...?'

Unable to speak, she could only nod her head. Her eyes were dazed with shock as she realised what she must have known for a long time—*she was in love with Brett*.

He touched her arm, his eyes warm with concern. 'I didn't think it would affect you like this. I'll get someone else to take over for you.'

'No, I'm all right,' she managed to say through stiff lips.

'Sure?'

'Quite sure.'

She walked away quickly, needing to be alone with her new self-knowledge, with the tumult of emotion raging inside her.

The wedding guests were making their way towards the main building where the reception was about to begin. Erin had to be there too. Her professional pride surfaced as she entered the room which had been decorated for the party, and saw the wedding cake and the other confections she had made. She had organised this reception—against her will, it was true—but she had done the best job she knew how, and she would see it through to the end. She could make a successful career for herself as a caterer, if that was what she wanted—Brett had been right about that.

Brett had been right about so many things.

Priscilla had a large family and Jim seemed to have many friends, so the party was a merry affair. Wine flowed amid speeches, toasts and dancing. When the time arrived for the wedding cake to be cut, Erin made certain she was near by in case of problems. Jim placed his hand over Priscilla's on the knife, and as the blade plunged into the cake they were both laughing. At the same moment they looked up. They saw Erin watching them, and their laughter stilled.

A sudden silence filled the room. It was as if the wedding guests, having watched the three-way exchange of looks, were uncomfortable and embarrassed.

Erin knew what she had to do.

She was smiling as she closed the gap between Jim and Priscilla and herself. Holding out her hands to them both, she said, 'Congratulations once again. I hope your future will be a happy one.'

'Thanks, Erin,' Jim muttered, his face red.

Priscilla only stared at her, her eyes wide and disbelieving.

The hubbub resumed as Erin walked away. Any moment now coffee would be served, and she made her way to the cake table. She was giving the tortes she had finished decorating last night a final look when two hands clasped her arms.

A familiar excitement shivered through her. For a moment she stood quite still, enjoying the warmth of the long fingers on her bare skin. Then she turned.

'I think everything's going well, Brett,' she said.

'More than well.' His eyes were on her face. 'Have I told you you're a classy woman, Erin?'

She smiled. 'I believe you have.'

'I'm telling you again now. You handled yourself magnificently.'

'Thank you, Brett.'

'You saved what could have been a very awkward moment. It couldn't have been easy to wish Jim and Priscilla well.'

'In the end, it wasn't all that difficult,' she admitted.

With her new-found love for Brett welling inside her, it was as much as Erin could trust herself to say.

Despite the fact that she had got to bed very late, Erin was up early the next morning. As the events of the previous day came back to her she pushed aside the sheets and flung open the windows. Mist hung over the tallest trees in the garden and the distant mountains were invisible. Not far from the rondavel was a frangipani—its flowers were white, its branches oddly contorted.

Beautiful during the day, in the grey light of dawn it looked like a plant from some other world.

Last night there had been a moment when Erin had known what she had to do. Now there was another such moment.

It did not take her long to pull on cords and a warm sweater. Outside it was cool, but she did not notice the chill as she hurried through the garden and made her way to the back of the hotel. Long before she reached the stables, she heard the sounds of the horses on the still air. On the dewy ground, a man's shoes had made their imprints.

Brett was stroking his horse, his hand running over its flanks in long fluid movements. Erin's heart raced as she watched him. She longed to feel his hands on her own skin, caressing her, making love to her, lifting her to heights to which only he could take her.

He had left the horse and was walking towards the saddles when she said, 'Brett...'

He turned. 'Hello, Erin.'

'Going for a ride?'

'Like to join me?'

'Very much,' she said.

She watched him readying the horses, her body thrilling to his nearness. She allowed him to help her on to the saddle, and wished she could prolong the touch of his hands on her waist. Keeping the horses to a slow walk, they left the stables and made their way along the trail that led away from the hotel.

'Care to try a new route today?' Brett asked.

'Why not?' she replied with a smile, knowing it did not matter very much where they went. She would be with the man she loved, and that was all that mattered.

For a while Brett led the way, then the trail widened, enabling them to ride alongside each other.

Erin started when he reached out and took her hand. 'You did a terrific job of the wedding,' he said.

'Thank you.'

'Was it the ordeal you thought it would be?'

She took her time about answering. There was a sensuous excitement about this ride—the two horses walking so close together; Erin's feet within touching distance of Brett's; his hand holding hers as they rode. She glanced at him and saw that he was watching her.

'I wanted to talk to you about that.' Her heart was in her throat, but she forced herself to go on. 'That's why I came out so early this morning. I had to find you.'

'What are you saying, Erin?' The dark eyes were alert.

'I was outraged when you forced me to bake for Jim's wedding, Brett. If I could have left Hilltop Inn then and there, I would have done so. I couldn't understand why you'd do such a thing to me. The night before the wedding, when you came to me in the kitchen, you said...you said you'd had a reason...that if I knew what it was I should tell you.'

'Do you know, Erin?'

'Yes, Brett, I think I do.' She looked at him, and wondered if the dim dawn light kept him from seeing the love in her eyes. 'I think you wanted me to come to terms with Jim's marriage. That you wanted me to understand what it really meant to me.'

'Did those things happen, Erin?' There was an urgency in his tone.

'Yes! It was so strange, Brett. I listened to Jim and Priscilla speaking their vows. I watched them kiss. And I felt nothing, absolutely nothing. Jim could have been some stranger—that's how detached I was from the whole thing. When I wished them well, those were not empty words I was saying. Suddenly I was seeing Priscilla with different eyes. I still don't think what Jim did was right, starting an affair with one woman when he was about to marry someone else, but perhaps they couldn't help falling in love.'

'That's very generous of you,' he commented.

'Something else was settled in my mind. I know now that I was never in love with Jim. We were attracted to each other, our romance was quick and lively and exciting, but all I ever felt for Jim—and perhaps he for me—was infatuation.'

'Well,' Brett drawled, an expression in his eyes that made Erin's blood run like fire in her veins, 'this is even more than I hoped for. What happens now?'

'I don't know what you mean,' she said.

'Still going back to Canada?'

She moved restlessly on her saddle. 'I have enough money now to pay for my flights.'

His hand tightened on hers. 'You haven't answered the question.'

She darted him a look from beneath her lashes. 'Haven't I?' she murmured.

She withdrew her hand from his then, tightened her legs on the saddle, and spurred her horse into a canter. Behind her she heard Brett laugh. He had caught up with her in seconds. And then they were cantering side by side on the misty trail.

CHAPTER TEN

LATER that day Brett gave Erin a cheque for her commission on the work she had done for the wedding. In the privacy of her rondavel, she added the amount to the balance in her bank book. At last she could afford to pay for her flights home.

On Tuesday she would drive to town, find a travel agent and plan the journey, she decided, trying to ignore a feeling of emptiness in her chest. But Tuesday came and went, without her making the trip to town. She did not go on Wednesday either, nor on any of the days that followed.

Brett did not ask her when she planned to buy her air tickets, and she did not volunteer the information.

There was a kind of magic in the time after Jim's wedding. There was also a sense of endings, which made every hour at Hilltop Inn precious. The tenor of the days changed. Every morning now there was the ride with Brett, along trails which Erin had never suspected existed. Side by side they would walk their horses, with the breeze blowing their hair and the long wild grasses swishing against the soles of their shoes. Brett would bring with him a flask and two cups, and they would stop at a stream or waterfall and drink their coffee, chatting as they watched the steam rise from their cups. There was so much to talk about: different childhoods, different schooling, different families; and the things they shared, such as music and books and a passionate love of animals and nature. It seemed as if they could never run out of topics to discuss.

The days were cooler now than they had been, shorter too, for winter was approaching, but the pool was heated, and Erin and Brett were able to end every evening with a swim. Later they would go to Erin's rondavel or to Brett's. Brett would build a log fire, and they would sit together and watch the flames.

Erin had a sense sometimes of being courted, but if that was so it was a strange kind of courting, for Brett did not try to make love to her again. It was as if the night of the scorpion or the day in the cabin had never happened.

There was never a moment when she was not conscious of her love for Brett. The knowledge that their parting was imminent was unbearably painful. Loving him as she did, she no longer wanted to leave Hilltop Inn. But Brett had never uttered one word of love, and Erin knew that she could not delay her departure indefinitely.

A week after Jim's wedding Wayne Anderson arrived at the hotel. The store was closed, for it was Sunday, and Erin, Brett and Wayne had a *braaivleis* in the garden.

They were finishing their meal when Wayne said, 'It's Amy's birthday next Thursday. She'll be five, and she's decided she wants a party. She wants to know if you'll make her a birthday cake, Erin.'

'I'd like that! I'll think of something special. And there'll be no charge, of course.'

Brett grinned. 'Now that Erin is a woman of means, she can afford to be generous.'

'It's very kind of you, Erin, but I can't ask you to go to all that trouble for nothing,' Wayne said. 'You must let me pay.'

'No way. Let it be my birthday present to Amy. I'm so fond of your children—you know that.'

Wayne smiled. 'I do know. Thanks, Erin. Listen, will you come out for the day? That was Amy's other request—that you spend her birthday at the farm.'

'No,' Brett said.

Erin turned her head to look at the man she loved. A few moments ago he had been smiling and relaxed. Now his expression was hard.

'It would mean so much to Amy,' Wayne continued, before Erin could speak. 'To all of us, actually. This will be Amy's first birthday without her mother present. It will be hard for Tim too.'

'Erin is not the mother of your children,' Brett pointed out.

'I know that, but having her at the farm would make things easier for us all.'

'It's out of the question,' said Brett.

'Why?' Erin asked, realising that she did not know him as well as she'd thought.

'Have you forgotten the store?'

'Would it matter if I closed it for one day?'

'Yes, it would.' Brett's tone was as hard as his eyes now. 'Erin's Place is a business. It's open at certain hours, and Thursday is a business day.'

'But, Brett, if people wanted to buy something and found the store closed, they could always come back the next day.'

'Not if they were leaving Hilltop Inn before the store re-opens.'

Erin looked at Wayne, saw the disappointment in his face, and was suddenly confused. Turning once more to Brett, she said, 'Do you think that perhaps you're being unreasonable?'

'No, Erin, I don't.'

'I'm sorry,' Wayne said quickly, 'I didn't mean to cause a problem. I'll explain to Amy and Tim why you won't be able to come, Erin, but if I could pick up the cake from you on Thursday morning that would be wonderful.'

'I'll have it ready for you,' she said, with a smile that hid her anger at Brett's inexplicable reaction.

The pleasant atmosphere of the *braaivleis* had given way to tension, and Erin was not surprised when Wayne got up to go.

When his car had driven out of the gates of the hotel, she looked at Brett. 'Wayne was disappointed,' she told him.

'I saw that.' His expression was grim.

'Would it really have been so bad if I'd closed Erin's Place for one day?'

'Yes.'

'Why, Brett?'

He looked at her, his eyes hooded. 'Wasn't the reason I gave you good enough?'

'I thought you could have made an exception of Amy's birthday.'

'No,' he said, 'I could not.'

'But Brett——'

'I don't want to discuss it any further,' he said.

Erin did not ride with Brett the next day. At dawn the day after that there was a knock on the door of her rondavel.

Brett stood on her doorstep, clad in riding breeches and a rough sweater.

'Coming out with me this morning, Erin?'

Loving him as she did, it was impossible for her to remain angry with him.

'Give me ten minutes,' she said.

'On second thoughts, you look very sexy in that flimsy thing you're wearing.' His hand brushed her throat in a caress that heated her blood. 'Maybe we should skip the ride.'

She swallowed on a surge of hot desire. She wanted nothing more than to draw him into the rondavel, but they had barely talked since the day when Brett had suddenly turned dictatorial, and Erin had a sense of this not being the right time for them to make love.

'I think a ride would be very nice,' she said tightly.

His eyes gleamed, almost as if he knew her thoughts and was amused by them. 'Meet you in the stables,' he said.

Both horses had been saddled by the time Erin joined Brett.

Lips tilting in a wicked grin, he looked down at her. 'You look sexy in riding gear too, Erin.'

She laughed up at him. 'Do you ever think about anything but sex, Brett?'

He pretended to think about that. 'Sometimes,' he said, and Erin laughed again.

They had left the hotel and were on one of their favourite trails when Brett said, 'I'm going away for a while.'

Erin looked at him, just a few feet away from her on the tall black horse which seemed to be his favourite. 'Oh?' she queried.

'I have some business to attend to.' He threw her a smile which made its way straight to her heart. 'Will you miss me?'

Erin wondered if her eyes revealed her feelings as she smiled back at him. Unreasonable as Brett had been in his reaction to Amy Anderson's birthday party, his place in her heart was becoming more firmly entrenched every day.

'I might,' she said lightly. 'How long will you be gone?'

'A few days.'

'A few days...' She drew a breath, then said the words she had been avoiding until now. 'I guess I should be thinking of some business of my own soon.'

'Business, Erin?' he queried.

'I should be seeing a travel agent, Brett.'

'Why don't we talk about that when I get back?'

It was not the response Erin had expected. From the start, Brett had tried to change her mind about returning to Canada, yet now that she was about to plan the trip her departure appeared to hold no more interest for him. The fact that she was ready to go did not seem to have upset him in the least.

She was glad when the trail narrowed seconds later, and Brett took the lead. Her eyes were filled with tears, so that she could barely make out the shape of the man ahead of her. It was unbearably painful to realise that her feelings were one-sided, that, whereas she loved Brett with all her heart, his own interest in her had never been based on more than sex.

Brett left the hotel at dawn on Wednesday. That evening Erin baked a cake for Amy. Made to look like a doll, with chocolate for hair, jelly beans for the eyes, a sliver of carrot for the mouth, and a dress of pale pink frosting, it was a cake a little girl would enjoy.

Next morning Erin dialled the number of the Anderson farm.

'Happy birthday, Amy,' she said, when the child answered the phone.

'Is that you, Erin?'

'Yes. How does it feel to be five years old?'

'OK.' But the little girl did not sound happy.

'Looking forward to your party, Amy?'

'Yes. Please come, Erin,' begged the little girl.

'I wish I could, honey, but I have to work.'

Amy did not answer, and Erin heard a muffled sob.

'Amy?' she said.

A second later Wayne was on the line. 'Sorry about that,' he said.

'Is Amy upset that I'm not coming out to the farm today?' asked Erin.

'I'm afraid so. I told her you couldn't make it, but she kept hoping you'd change your mind.'

'I wish I could be there, but you know how Brett feels about closing the store.'

'He made that clear, didn't he?'

'You'll make it a good party, Wayne.'

'I'll try my darnedest, but at times like these the kids miss their mother.'

'I'm not their mother,' Erin said gently.

'You're a woman, Erin—a warm, lovely woman. And Amy and Tim are very fond of you.'

Erin stared into the phone. 'When will you come for the cake, Wayne?' she asked.

'I'll be leaving the farm within the hour,' he said.

The idea came to Erin as she was putting the cake in a carton. Picking up the phone once more, she dialled the reception desk and asked Liz for a number. Then she made one more call.

When Wayne arrived she was waiting for him, cake carton in hand, tote bag slung over her shoulder.

Her eyes were sparkling. 'I'm coming with you,' she announced.

Wayne was taken aback. 'Brett won't like that.'

'I can't bear to think about Amy being upset,' she explained.

'What about Brett, Erin?'

'He didn't want the store closed, but it suddenly occurred to me that I could get someone else to work in my place. You must know Gloria—the girl who fills in for Liz on weekends? I phoned her, and she was quite happy to look after Erin's Place for me today.'

'Wonderful!' exclaimed Wayne. A moment later he had taken the carton from Erin's hands and was opening the door so that she could get into the car.

Amy and Tim were playing in the yard when Erin and Wayne arrived at the farm. They looked up as the car stopped. Tim saw Erin first. He grabbed his sister's arm and pointed. By the time Erin's door was open, both children were racing towards her.

'Hi, Tim. Happy birthday, Amy.' Erin bent to hug them both.

'You came!' Amy looked ecstatic. 'Erin, you came!'

Over the heads of the children, Erin exchanged a look with their father. He was smiling, but his eyes looked suspiciously bright. Erin bent once more and put a gift in Amy's hands. The little girl was thrilled with a book of illustrated folk stories, and both children exclaimed with glee over the cake.

Erin had remembered to bring her bikini, and they all spent the morning swimming. Later, Erin and Wayne lay back on long chairs in the shade.

'I'll miss this beautiful countryside when I go,' Erin said, her eyes on the distant mountains.

Wayne looked at her curiously. 'You're still determined to leave us, then?'

'I have to.'

'I believe you'd rather stay,' he remarked.

'My home is in Canada,' Erin said firmly.

'I think your heart is in Africa.'

Erin's eyes left the mountains as she swung her head around to look at Wayne. 'What do you mean by that?' she queried.

'You're in love with Brett, aren't you?'

'How did you know?' she whispered.

'I guessed.'

'You *did*?'

'Why do you think I haven't made a move on you myself, Erin? I'd like nothing more than to ask you to marry me, but I've always known what your answer would be.'

'You don't love me, Wayne,' she told him.

'Not as a woman deserves to be loved,' he admitted honestly.

'Your heart is still with your wife. If you were to be married at this stage, it would only be because you wanted someone to mother your children.'

'There is that,' he said. 'But to get back to you, Erin, why leave if you love Brett?'

'My feelings aren't reciprocated.'

'Are you certain of that?'

'At one time I thought they might be, but I know now that I was wrong.' She stood up abruptly. 'If you don't mind, I'd rather not talk about Brett. Amy's friends will be arriving soon. Shall we have another swim before the party begins?'

By three o'clock a dozen children had arrived at the farm. Amy was in her element—opening gifts, leading her friends in different games, blowing out the five candles on the cake Erin had baked for her. Without being intrusive, Erin and Wayne hovered near by, offering help or mediation when either was required, enjoying Amy's happiness.

When the last child had left the farm, Erin said, 'Did you have a good time, Amy?'

'Oh, yes! I'm so glad you came, Erin.'

'I am too. Thanks for inviting me, honey.'

'I'm going to drive Erin back to Hilltop Inn now,' said Wayne. 'If you've both had your baths by the time I get back, I'll read you a story from Erin's book.'

Erin gave each child a hug, then followed him out of the farmhouse and into the yard.

They were at the car when she said, 'You're lucky to have such lovely children.'

'I only wish Mary could have lived to watch them grow up.' Wayne sounded so sad.

She put her hand on his arm. 'You're a wonderful father. Amy enjoyed her birthday very much.'

'More so because you were here. Last year Mary...' His voice was choked. 'Thank you for coming, Erin.'

'Wayne...' she began, seeing the tears in his eyes.

'I'll be all right.' Without warning, he drew her into his arms and held her close. 'Your presence here made the day easier for me too,' he said against her ear.

Feeling him trembling against her, Erin did not attempt to draw away from him. She understood that he was overwhelmed by grief, and that he was in need of comfort.

She could not have said afterwards how long they stood wrapped in each other's arms, but all at once she felt Wayne stiffen. Puzzled, she lifted her head to look at him. And then, her glance following the direction of his, she saw a tall figure step away from the shadows where his car was parked.

'*Brett*!' she exclaimed. 'What on earth are you doing here? I didn't think you'd be back before tomorrow.'

'I finished my business today.'

'We didn't hear you arrive.'

'I'd just stopped the car when you came out of the house.' Brett's tone was harder than Erin had ever heard it.

'Why didn't you call out?' she asked, feeling suddenly uneasy.

'And spoil that touching scene?'

'You don't understand——' Wayne began.

'I think I understand all I need to.'

'Amy's party just ended, and I was about to drive Erin back to the hotel. When you saw us, I was telling her that I——'

Brett did not let him finish. 'Your conversation doesn't interest me in the least. I'm on my way back to the hotel myself, so I'll take Erin with me and save you the trip.'

'Brett——' Wayne said.

'Come along, Erin.' The words had the sound of an order.

As the car left the farm road and turned on to the highway, Erin tried to control her trembling. She did not trust herself to speak, but now and then she stole a sideways glance at Brett. She could not see his eyes, but his profile was forbidding.

The miles sped by. Fifteen minutes passed. In the car there was silence.

It was only when Erin felt that she could talk with confidence that she turned to Brett. 'Would you like to tell me why you're so angry?' she asked quietly.

'I hardly think you need telling.'

'Tell me anyway.'

'I told you not to go to the farm today, Erin.'

'You said you wanted the store kept open. It was. I asked Gloria to cover for me. You'd have known that if you'd gone to the hotel before driving out to the farm.'

'I was at the hotel.' Brett's tone was even harsher than before. 'I went to the store and found you missing.'

Erin stared uncomprehendingly at the man she loved, searching his face for some kind of gentleness, some reminder of the passion and tenderness they had shared. But there was only the unyielding hardness.

'If you were at the store, then you must have seen Gloria.'

'I should have seen *you*, Erin.'

'Surely the point was that Erin's Place was to be open for business?'

'The point,' Brett said, his voice clipped, 'is that I pay you to run that store. The point, also, is that I expressly told you that you were not to go to Amy's birthday, and you decided to go notwithstanding.'

Erin was suddenly very angry. 'You make me sound like a slave.'

'Do I?' he drawled.

'I may be your employee, Brett—and thank you for reminding me of that fact, because there have been times when I was in danger of forgetting it—but I'm also a person of some discretion. I understood that you wanted the store open, but I decided it was fine to leave it in Gloria's hands. And, in case you're wondering who'll pay her for the day's work, I will. My escapade today won't cost you a cent.'

'You could have asked me what I thought about it, Erin. Why didn't you?'

'You weren't here to ask. I only made the decision this morning.'

'I suppose Wayne talked you into it?'

'It was my decision all the time.' She looked at him squarely. 'And if you're thinking of firing me, Brett, you can save yourself the trouble. Tomorrow I'll see about booking my trip back home. I should never have waited as long as I did.'

Erin sometimes went into town on a Friday so that she could replenish her baking supplies. She was never gone for very long, and there was always a note on the door of Erin's Place informing potential customers when the doors of the store would re-open.

Shortly after noon on the day after Amy's birthday, she took the Honda from the garage. On her way down the drive she caught sight of Brett. It was the first time she had seen him since their return from Wayne's farm, but she did not stop to speak to him. Though she saw him look her way she did not even lift her hand in greeting.

Erin was a conscientious driver, but that day she drove a little too fast. With her decision made, she wanted only to find a travel agent, pay for her tickets, and make plans to depart from Hilltop Inn as soon as possible. The thought of leaving Brett was unbearably painful, but there was no point in remaining in a place where she would be reminded anew every day of his arrogance.

She came to the town and parked the car. Heavy feet took her along the street to a travel agency's door. The consultants were busy, and Erin had to wait some time for her turn. When a consultant was free, and beckoned to her, she felt a little ill. Tears filled her eyes, and she almost turned and walked out of the agency. But strength of will came to her rescue, and the knowledge that there was nothing else she could do, and she forced her feet to the counter.

She told the consultant her plans, and the woman studied schedules and worked out a fare. Then she looked at Erin, her eyes compassionate as she took in the girl's obvious distress.

'I can write out the details of the trip, Miss Leroy,' she said. 'Perhaps you'd like to study them for a while before you make up your mind?'

Erin swallowed back her tears. 'There's nothing to think about,' she said.

'Do you want me to write out the ticket now?'

'Yes,' Erin said.

'No,' said someone else, almost at the same moment.

The consultant looked confused. She glanced at Erin, then they both looked at the man who had appeared at the counter.

Brett put his hand on Erin's arm. 'Don't write out the ticket,' he said to the consultant.

'Miss Leroy...?' The woman was looking at Erin for guidance.

'My instructions stand,' Erin said, but faintly.

'Don't write out the ticket,' Brett said again. He looked at Erin. 'At least let us talk first.'

Erin swallowed hard. With Brett's unexpected arrival, the last bit of colour had drained from her face, and her legs were so weak that she thought she would fall.

'Perhaps you really should consider your plans a while longer, Miss Leroy.' The consultant's tone was understanding.

Erin shook her head. 'That won't be necessary.'

'Give us some time,' Brett said. 'If my...if Miss Leroy is still of the same mind in half an hour, she'll be back.'

Not wishing to make even more of a scene in front of curious bystanders, Erin was silent as she followed Brett out of the travel agency. Once on the street, however, she threw him a furious look.

'How dare you humiliate me like that?' she snapped.

'There's nothing stopping you from buying your ticket half an hour from now,' he pointed out.

'I intend to buy it immediately!'

Brett's face was oddly pale beneath his tan, and there were lines of tension around his eyes which Erin had never seen before.

'Half an hour of your time is all I ask, Erin.'

'Half an hour,' she agreed after a moment.

She allowed him to lead her to a nearby restaurant. She had reached a point where protest would have been impossible even if she had had the strength for it.

The restaurant was almost empty at that time of the day. They took a table in the corner, and did not speak until the waitress had brought them coffee.

'I'm sorry,' Brett said then. 'I'm so sorry, Erin.'

'For what?' she asked unsteadily.

'For the way I behaved yesterday. I hope you can forgive me.'

'Why were you so angry, Brett? I still don't understand.'

Leaning across the table, he took one of her hands in his. 'I felt threatened,' he told her.

'*Threatened*?'

'By Wayne.'

Erin stared at him in confusion. 'But my going to the farm had nothing to do with Wayne. I only went because Amy seemed to need me.'

'I know that now. Wayne phoned me this morning—he seemed to think it was something I should know. I was on my way to talk to you when you shot past in the car. It didn't take much guesswork to know where you were going, my darling.'

My darling... The endearment was so unexpected that Erin trembled.

'You're here because Wayne spoke to you, Brett?'

'I would have come anyway. Erin ... My darling Erin, you don't know how difficult our time together has been for me. There you were, never quite knowing whether you'd got over Jim or not, insisting that you wouldn't let yourself fall in love again. Certain that if you did let a man into your life it could only be on the rebound.'

'What are you saying?' she whispered.

'I fell in love with you the first day I met you.'

'I don't believe it!' She looked at him, stunned.

'I let myself believe that the attraction was mutual, that you felt something for me too. But after the way Jim had treated you, you weren't about to trust yourself to another man in a hurry.'

'That's true...'

'I knew I had to be patient, let enough time go by before I could tell you how I felt. I kept wondering when you'd realise that your feelings for Jim were dead, that all you'd ever felt for him in the first place was infatuation.'

'You got me to bake for his wedding...'

'You thought I was a brute, and perhaps I was, but it was the only way. I knew I was risking your hatred, but I had to force you to face up to your feelings.'

'Which I did,' Erin agreed.

'I was so happy when you finally told me that you'd never loved Jim. I knew that the moment had come for us, my darling. I would have liked to propose to you then and there, but I made up my mind to take things slowly. Your time with Jim was too hurried, and I didn't want that to happen with us. I thought it would be best if we spent time together, got to know each other. I decided to court you, woo you. I hoped you'd begin to love me as much as I loved you.'

As Erin listened to Brett, barely able to believe his outpouring of words, a great happiness grew inside her, pushing out her despair.

'The moment came,' Brett went on, 'when I thought you were ready. I told you I was going away on business, but actually I was on my way to buy something for you. Something that would show you how much I loved you. And then Wayne arrived and asked you to spend the day at the farm.'

'Wayne never meant anything to me, Brett,' she said earnestly.

'I wasn't sure about that. Not then, anyway. Wayne Anderson is an attractive man, Erin. You were clearly taken with his children, and they with you. For all I knew, you might have agreed to marry him and be a mother for Amy and Tim.'

'But Brett——'

'I couldn't risk that, my darling. I'd been too patient, I'd waited too long, only to lose you when I was about to tell you that I loved you.'

'So that's why you forbade me to go to the farm,' Erin realised.

'Can you imagine how I felt when I returned to the hotel and found you gone? And then to arrive at the farm and see you in Wayne's arms? It was more than I could bear, Erin.'

'That embrace didn't mean anything, Brett. Wayne was grieving for his wife, and I was giving him comfort.'

'He told me that too.' Brett glanced at his watch. 'My half-hour is going by too quickly.'

Erin threw him a mischievous look. 'In the circumstances, I think I could grant you an extension.'

'My darling Erin!' Brett's voice was suddenly ragged. 'Let me show you what I have for you.'

As he put a small velvet-covered box on the table beside her, her heart began a painful thudding.

'Open it,' he said softly.

Her fingers trembled as she picked up the box. She opened it slowly, gasping when she saw what lay inside.

A ring. An antique ring, its central diamond surrounded by tiny sapphires.

'Do you like it, Erin?' asked Brett quietly.

'It's the most beautiful thing I've ever seen.' Her eyes had filled with tears and her voice shook.

'Will you let me put it on for you, darling?'

Erin could only nod.

'Tell me first—will you marry me, Erin?'

'Yes, my darling, I will. I love you, Brett. I love you so much.'

'Then you won't go back to Canada?'

'Only with you, Brett. For a holiday, and so that my family can meet you.'

'Give me your left hand, darling,' Brett said, and slipped the ring on to the third finger.

He had leaned forward to kiss her, when the waitress appeared with more coffee. She looked at the radiant couple, so absorbed in their own private world, then she walked away quietly, allowing them to enjoy their happiness.

Accept 4 FREE Romances and 2 FREE gifts

FROM READER SERVICE

An irresistible invitation from Mills & Boon Reader Service. Please accept our offer of 4 free Romances, a CUDDLY TEDDY and a special MYSTERY GIFT... Then, if you choose, go on to enjoy 6 captivating Romances every month for just £1.70 each, postage and packing free. Plus our FREE Newsletter with author news, competitions and much more.

Send the coupon below to:
Reader Service, FREEPOST,
PO Box 236, Croydon,
Surrey CR9 9EL.

NO STAMP REQUIRED

Yes! Please rush me 4 Free Romances and 2 free gifts!
Please also reserve me a Reader Service Subscription. If I decide to subscribe I can look forward to receiving 6 brand new Romances each month for just £10.20, post and packing free.
If I choose not to subscribe I shall write to you within 10 days - I can keep the books and gifts whatever I decide. I may cancel or suspend my subscription at any time. I am over 18 years of age.

Ms/Mrs/Miss/Mr ——————————————————— EP30R

Address ————————————————————

————————————————————————

Postcode——————— Signature ——————

Next Month's Romances

Each month you can choose from a wide variety of romance with Mills & Boon. Below are the new titles to look out for next month, why not ask either Mills & Boon Reader Service or your Newsagent to reserve you a copy of the titles you want to buy — just tick the titles you would like and either post to Reader Service or take it to any Newsagent and ask them to order your books.

Please save me the following titles:	Please tick	√
BABY MAKES THREE	Emma Goldrick	
BETH AND THE BARBARIAN	Miranda Lee	
GRACIOUS LADY	Carole Mortimer	
THE HAWK AND THE LAMB	Susan Napier	
VIKING MAGIC	Angela Wells	
DECEPTIVE PASSION	Sophie Weston	
LOVE ON LOAN	Natalie Fox	
EDGE OF WILDNESS	Christine Greig	
LEARNING TO LOVE	Rosemary Hammond	
PASSIONATE ADVENTURE	Karen van der Zee	
THE BECKONING FLAME	Jessica Hart	
TOO SCARED TO LOVE	Cathy Williams	
NO GOING BACK	Stephanie Howard	
PORTRAIT OF CLEO	Joanna Mansell	
BAY OF RAINBOWS	Dana James	
A WARNING OF MAGIC	Kate Kingston	

If you would like to order these books in addition to your regular subscription from Mills & Boon Reader Service please send £1.70 per title to: Mills & Boon Reader Service, Freepost, P.O. Box 236, Croydon, Surrey, CR9 9EL, quote your Subscriber No:.................................... (If applicable) and complete the name and address details below. Alternatively, these books are available from many local Newsagents including W.H.Smith, J.Menzies, Martins and other paperback stockists from 9th April 1993.

Name:...

Address:...

....Post Code:.........................

To Retailer: If you would like to stock M&B books please contact your regular book/magazine wholesaler for details.

You may be mailed with offers from other reputable companies as a result of this application. If you would rather not take advantage of these opportunities please tick box ☐